RESTAURANT TECHNOLOGY

Revolutionizing
Quick Service Restaurants

CK CHONG

RESTAURANT TECHNOLOGY

REVOLUTIONIZING

QUICK SERVICE RESTAURANTS

CK CHONG

Table of Contents

Foreword

Restaurant Tech: Revolutionizing Quick Service Restaurants

This book encompasses the gold standard for Restaurant Technology (RestTech). In an era where technology drives Quick Service Restaurants (QSRs), this book is a compass for food & beverage operators, innovators, digital transformation professionals, and enthusiasts alike.

It defines RestTech standards, guiding QSR professionals to harness the power of digitalization, data, and innovation. The author's wealth of experience spanning global multinational giants and iconic QSR brands forms the cornerstone for a comprehensive guide that promises to reshape the way the industry leverages technology and data. This book isn't just a reference; it's a roadmap for QSR or any retail pioneers ready to embark on a digital revolution.

About the Author

Author: CK Chong
Email: mychongck@gmail.com
LinkedIn: https://www.linkedin.com/in/ck-chong

About the Author

CK Chong is very passionate and an expert in the field of technology, with extensive work experience in multinational corporations. His contributions to the industry have made him a notable figure in the world of IT applications and digital transformation.

CK's career journey began in 1990 when he graduated with a Computer Science and Mathematics Bachelor of Science degree from Campbell University. At the same time, he obtained his Diploma in Computer Science. Currently, he is in pursuit of a Master of Data Science, demonstrating his commitment to lifelong learning and staying at the forefront of technology.

CK's professional journey spans an impressive 35 years, during which he held various roles and positions in renowned multinational companies. His diverse experience spans companies such as Glaxo SmithKline, Reckitt Benckiser, Keystone Foods, IDS Medical, and QSR Brands. Throughout his career, Chong played pivotal roles in the regional and global rollout of core IT applications, particularly in the Asia Pacific and Eastern Europe regions.

His key achievements include:

- **McDonald's APMEA Regional Supply Chain**
  Notably, CK spent seven years working for Keystone Foods, where he contributed significantly to McDonald's APMEA's regional supply chain organization. His expertise in QSR supply chain integration and food logistic technology implementation greatly improved the efficiency and effectiveness of the food supply chain.
- **KFC and Pizza Hut Digital Transformation**
  CK in his role as Group Chief Information Officer in QSR Brands Group, where he devoted more than six years to driving the digital transformation of iconic brands of KFC and Pizza Hut. This phase of his career is focused on restaurant technology, digital commerce, and supply chain integration platforms. Under his leadership, these brands adapted to the evolving consumer landscape, embracing technology to enhance the customer experience and streamline operations.

CK's vast knowledge and hands-on experience in restaurant technology led him to write a groundbreaking book on the subject. Titled " Restaurant Technology: Revolutionizing Quick Service Restaurants", his book serves as a comprehensive guide for industry professionals, digital transformation advocates, and enthusiasts alike. In this book, he delves into the intricacies of digital transformation within the quick-service restaurant industry, exploring how IT applications can revolutionize dining experiences.

CK's journey from his educational background to his illustrious career in multinational corporations and eventual authorship of this book displays a remarkable dedication to advancing the field. His expertise in IT applications, digital transformation, and restaurant technology has undoubtedly left an indelible mark on the industry. As the restaurant sector continues to evolve in response to technological advancements, CK's work remains a valuable resource and source of inspiration for those seeking to innovate and excel in this dynamic field.

He can be reached for readers' comments, feedback, and sharing of thoughts through his email and public LinkedIn profile.

Acknowledgments

As I stand at the completion of this book, I'm humbled by the journey it represents—a journey of innovation, resilience, and unwavering support. To all those who have been an integral part of this endeavor, I extend my deepest gratitude.

First and foremost, I'd like to express my heartfelt thanks to my incredible digital team members in QSR Brands and partners from Yum! Brands and McDonald's. Your dedication, passion, and tireless effort in the ever-evolving world of Restaurant Technology have been instrumental in bringing this vision to life. Your commitment to excellence is truly inspiring.

I must also acknowledge our partners and vendors, who stood by us during both good and challenging times, including the tumultuous days of the COVID-19 pandemic. Your collaboration and solidarity have been pivotal in sustaining our business and leadership in the industry.

Special thanks to Ronald Chong for his significant contribution in completing the manuscript.

To my lovely wife, Yoke Cheng, and our children, your unwavering support, understanding, and patience have been my anchor throughout this journey. Your sacrifices and encouragement have enabled me to dedicate myself to this work.

With heartfelt thanks,

CK Chong

The Book at a Glance

I wrote this book to serve as a comprehensive guide for you as a reader to navigate the digital frontier with confidence and ingenuity.

Chapter 1: Introduction to RestTech Transformation

In this chapter, we'll delve into the digital disruption that has swept through the Quick Service Restaurants (QSR) industry. We'll discuss the need to adopt innovative technologies like omni-channel solutions, e-commerce integration, and advanced kitchen systems to stay competitive in the modern landscape.

Chapter 2: Core Component of RestTech

This chapter highlights some of the key components of RestTech. Many visuals are provided to showcase their real-life implementations and use cases. Further elaboration will be provided to highlight some of the best practices in implementation.

Chapter 3: Operational Challenges and RestTech Solutions

Operational challenges in the QSR industry are mitigated by employing digital solutions. These solutions encompass data-driven inventory management, streamlined order processing, personalized customer engagement, optimized staff training, and real-time feedback mechanisms. By integrating digital technologies, QSRs enhance efficiency, accuracy, customer experiences, and overall operational excellence.

Chapter 4: The Power of Omnichannel Experience

Explore how QSR giants like KFC, McDonald's, Pizza Hut, Domino's, Subway, Burger King, and Starbucks have harnessed the potential of omnichannel platforms to seamlessly engage with customers across various touchpoints. Learn about the convergence of physical and digital spaces, the role of mobile apps, self-service kiosks, and online ordering in creating a unified customer journey.

Chapter 5: Revolutionizing E-commerce Integration

Dive into the world of e-commerce and how it has reshaped the QSR industry. Discover how brands are leveraging online ordering/delivery platforms and integrated payment systems to enhance customer convenience and streamline operations. We'll also explore strategies for managing delivery logistics effectively and leveraging partnerships with food aggregators.

Chapter 6: Mastering the Restaurant Kitchen System

This chapter delves into the heart of QSR operations: the kitchen. Explore cutting-edge kitchen management systems that optimize efficiency, reduce errors, and improve consistency in the food preparation process. We'll cover topics such as order automation, inventory management, and real-time data synchronization between the kitchen and front-end operations.

Chapter 7: Crafting a Data Strategy for Success

Data is the lifeblood of modern businesses. Learn how QSRs can harness customer data to gain insights into preferences, behaviors, and trends. In this chapter, we explore methods for collecting, analyzing, and interpreting data to make informed business decisions that drive growth and competitiveness.

Chapter 8: Building a Customer Data Platform (CDP)

Creating a centralized repository for customer data is crucial. Discover the concept of a Customer Data Platform (CDP) and how QSRs can utilize it to deliver personalized experiences, targeted marketing campaigns, and loyalty programs. We'll discuss data privacy considerations and the importance of ethical data usage.

Chapter 9: The Role of Marketing Technology (MarTech)

Explore the intersection of marketing and technology in the QSR realm. In this Marketing Technology (MarTech) topic, we learn about geotargeting, AI-driven recommendation engines, and social media engagement strategies that enable brands to reach the right audience with the right messages at the right time.

Chapter 10: Harnessing the Cloud Advantage

Cloud technology has transformed how businesses operate and scale. This chapter examines the benefits of adopting cloud platforms for QSRs, including increased flexibility, scalability, and data security. We'll also explore the role of cloud-based POS systems in simplifying operations.

Chapter 11: Implementation Strategy: Navigating Change

Transitioning to a tech driven QSR model requires careful planning. This chapter provides a step-by-step guide to implementing RestTech solutions, from selecting the right vendors to training staff and managing change resistance. My own experiences and case studies from industry leaders will offer practical insights.

Chapter 12: Food Delivery System

A food delivery system is a digital platform that coordinates and optimizes the end-to-end process of receiving, processing, and delivering customer orders. It includes online ordering interfaces, order routing, real-time tracking, and communication tools for seamless coordination between the restaurant, delivery personnel, and customers. This system ensures efficient order fulfillment, enhances delivery accuracy, and provides customers with a convenient and transparent food delivery experience.

Chapter 13: The Future Trends of RestTech

In this final chapter, we'll gaze into the future of RestTech and discuss emerging trends such as AI-powered chatbots, virtual reality dining experiences, and sustainable technologies. By staying ahead of the curve, QSRs can continue to innovate and delight customers in an ever-evolving digital landscape.

RestTech is the forefront digital touchpoint for QSR brands.
(Credit: McDonald's UAE)

Chapter 1:
Introduction to RestTech Transformation

In the fast-paced world of Quick Service Restaurants (QSR), where speed, efficiency, and customer satisfaction are paramount, the landscape is undergoing a radical transformation phase through the integration of cutting-edge Restaurant Technology (RestTech). This chapter sets the stage by highlighting the driving forces behind the RestTech revolution and the importance for QSR giants such as KFC, McDonald's, Pizza Hut, Taco Bell, Chipotle, Subway, Burger King, and Starbucks to embrace these advancements.

The following chart is the world's top 10 QSR operators by revenue as published by Verdict Food Services (based on 2019 revenue):
1. Starbucks
2. McDonald's
3. Subway
4. Yum China
5. Darden Restaurants
6. Restaurant Brands International
7. Yum! Brands
8. Chipotle Mexican Grill
9. Autogrill
10. Zensho Holdings

One of the notable and common features of these brands is that they are the leaders when it comes to RestTech adoption and innovation.

The Digital Disruption and A New Era for QSRs

In our lifetime, notice that the QSR industry is undergoing a profound transformation driven by digital disruption around us. Traditional QSR models are evolving into tech-savvy, customer-centric enterprises, heralding a new era for the industry.

Digital disruption comprises the widespread adoption of RestTech, such as mobile apps, e-commerce, in-store digital ordering channels, and AI-powered customer experiences. This technology empowers customers with convenience, experience personalization, and real-time access to menus and promotions.

In this new era, QSRs are leveraging data analytics to understand customer preferences, optimize menus, and enhance supply chain logistics and kitchen efficiencies. They're adopting contactless payment methods, integrating delivery services, and implementing self-service kiosks to streamline operations and improve efficiency.

Moreover, digital disruption has redefined customer expectations. Speed, convenience, and digital interactions have become key to staying competitive. QSRs that adapt and excel in providing these qualities will thrive in this new landscape.

This digital disruption isn't just a shift in technology; it's a change in the entire QSR business model. It's about reimagining customer journeys, redefining operational processes, and embracing innovation to stay ahead in an increasingly tech-driven world. The QSRs that embrace this disruption are poised to shape a new and exciting era for the industry, one defined by digital innovation, customer empowerment, and exceptional dining experiences.

The power of omnichannel, a QSR brand's customer digital touchpoint
(Credit: KFC Malaysia)

From Brick-and-Mortar to Omnichannel, The Evolution of Dining

Recalling my childhood experiences dining at a fast-food restaurant, the setting back then began with a traditional shop lot with just a few cashier counters, joining the long queue, and staring at the paper card menu.

In contrast to those days, the QSR landscape has witnessed a vast scale of transformation, shifting from traditional brick-and-mortar establishments to a dynamic omnichannel dining experience. This evolution reflects changing consumer expectations and the integration of technology into the overall dining experience.

Traditionally, QSRs solely relied on physical storefronts for customer engagement. Customers would visit these establishments in person to queue up, place orders, and finally dine in or opt for takeout. However, the digital age has ushered in a new era of dining.

Today, QSRs offer customers a seamless omnichannel experience. This covers a multi-pronged approach, including mobile apps for convenient ordering, delivery services for enjoying QSR cuisine at home or office, and self-service kiosks for in-store efficiency. Online platforms also provide access to digital menus, promotions, and loyalty programs, enhancing customer engagement.

The evolution to omnichannel dining empowers customers with choice and convenience, allowing them to interact with QSR brands through their preferred channels. Whether it's ordering through a mobile app, enjoying a meal in-store, or having food delivered to their doorstep, QSRs now cater to diverse customer preferences.

This transformation not only reflects the adaptability of QSRs but also underscores the critical role of technology in reshaping the dining experience. As QSRs continue to innovate and leverage RestTech solutions, the evolution towards omnichannel dining is likely to remain a central theme, ensuring that customers enjoy greater flexibility and accessibility in their dining choices.

The ever-evolving QSR industry (Credit: McDonald's Edinburgh)

Building Customer Relationships in a Digital Age

The core of the RestTech transformation is the concept of customer-centricity. Building customer relationships in the digital age is a delicate fusion of technology and brand emotions. Technologies such as mobile apps and online platforms provide unprecedented opportunities for QSRs like McDonald's, KFC, and Starbucks to connect with customers on a personal level. Through personalized promotions, loyalty programs, and user-friendly interfaces, digital channels allow for tailored interactions that resonate with individual preferences. All these are achieved through the app in the pocket.

However, it's equally vital to infuse brand emotions into these interactions. QSRs must convey the same warmth, reliability, and most importantly satisfaction in the digital realm that customers experience in physical restaurants. Be it through friendly app interfaces, authentic messaging, or consistently excellent service, brand emotions are the intangible elements that evoke trust and loyalty in a digital age, ensuring that customers feel not just connected but emotionally attached to the QSR brand.

RestTech helps build intimate and frictionless ordering moments with customers. (Credit: Taco Bell China)

Operational Efficiency and Innovation

The advantage of RestTech isn't just about improving customer experiences; it's about enhancing operational efficiency and creating a super-efficient kitchen, which is the backbone of QSR services.

- **Operation Efficiency**

  RestTech allows QSRs to allocate staff resources more effectively. Automated order processing reduces the need for manual order taking, enabling employees to focus on food preparation and customer service, while predictive analytics aids in inventory planning, and workforce scheduling, ensuring adequate staffing during peak hours. Mobile apps for staff enable quicker communication and order management. Digital apps can be deployed to ensure critical food safety routines are fully complied with, such as routine kitchen cleaning and regulatory compliance daily inspections. These staffing efficiencies optimize labor costs while maintaining service quality.

- **Kitchen Efficiency**

  RestTech optimizes kitchen operations through digital order management systems, automated cooking equipment, and predictive cooking control. Meanwhile, digital screens display orders, reducing errors and wait times, while smart appliances monitor cooking times and temperatures, ensuring consistent quality. Inventories are then managed in real-time using a cloud inventory management system, preventing wastage. These innovations minimize bottlenecks, improve order accuracy, and accelerate service, enhancing customer satisfaction.

Incorporating RestTech innovations in both kitchen and staffing operations elevates QSRs' operational efficiency, leading to faster service, reduced costs, and improved customer experiences.

In peak hours, digital channel helps in ordering while restaurant crews can focus on preparing food. (Credit: Burger King UK)

Staying Relevant in a Competitive Landscape

There is an urgency for large-scale QSR brands to adopt RestTech solutions to remain competitive. In the dynamic realm of the quick service industry, staying relevant is not just a goal; it's a survival imperative. The QSR landscape is fiercely competitive, marked by evolving consumer preferences, technological advancements, and shifting market dynamics. To thrive in this environment, QSRs must embrace innovation on multiple fronts.

Firstly, the integration of RestTech components is non-negotiable. Digital storefronts, mobile apps, and online ordering platforms have become standard, enhancing customer convenience and operational efficiency. Secondly, personalization is key. Data-driven insights enable tailored promotions, menu recommendations, and implementation of loyalty schemes.

Moreover, sustainability initiatives resonate with today's conscious consumers. QSRs can adopt eco-friendly practices, such as sustainable sourcing and reduced packaging waste, to appeal to environmentally aware customers.

In short, QSRs must adapt, innovate, and prioritize customer-centricity to remain relevant. Embracing digitalization, personalization, and sustainability can help navigate the competitive landscape and secure a lasting place in the hearts of consumers.

Chapter 2:
Core Component of RestTech

Definition of RestTech

Restaurant technology, often referred to as **RestTech** in this book, encompasses a diverse array of digital solutions that revolutionize the way restaurants operate, interact with customers through digital touchpoints, and adapt to the dynamic landscape of the food service industry. It encompasses a range of tools, software, and innovations designed to enhance efficiency, improve customer engagement, and drive growth within the restaurant ecosystem.

At its core, RestTech leverages digital advancements to optimize various aspects of restaurant operations. From streamlined order processing and efficient kitchen management to personalized customer interactions and data-driven decision-making, RestTech empowers restaurants to remain competitive and relevant in an increasingly digital world.

One key facet of RestTech is the integration of digital touchpoints for customers. Mobile apps, online ordering platforms, and self-service kiosks allow customers to interact with menus, place orders, and make payments seamlessly. This convenience not only enhances the customer experience but also reduces wait times, minimizes errors, and offers customization options.

The kitchen is another area profoundly impacted by RestTech. Advanced kitchen systems incorporate automation, real-time data synchronization, and inventory management tools to optimize food preparation, ensure consistency, and minimize waste. This translates into faster service and improved food quality, elevating overall customer satisfaction.

Crucially, RestTech revolves around data. Customer preferences, behaviors, and transaction histories are collected and analyzed to tailor offerings and marketing strategies. Data insights drive decisions, enabling restaurants to refine menus, craft personalized promotions, and implement efficient staffing solutions. The technology around data utilization and marketing execution is known as Marketing Technology or referred to as MarTech.

Security and privacy are paramount in this digital age, and RestTech addresses these concerns through secure payment gateways, data encryption, and compliance with regulations. This ensures that customer data is safeguarded while enabling meaningful engagement.

State-of-the-Art RestTech Ecosystem & Architecture

The illustration below provides an overview of the various RestTech ecosystem and architecture components. As highlighted, there are four major RestTech Components:

1. **Omnichannel**: Various in-store customer touchpoints and digital channels.
2. **Digital Commerce**: The above-the-store e-commerce, apps, and digital marketing platforms.
3. **Connected Restaurant**: Back-of-house restaurant operating system.
4. **Operation Excellence**: Various head office back-office support systems.

In the modern RestTech architecture, there is a need for Cloud Platform, Data & API Hub, and Marketing Technology (MarTech) Platforms to achieve maximum efficiencies and scalability. We will delve into the individual components in greater detail in the following chapters.

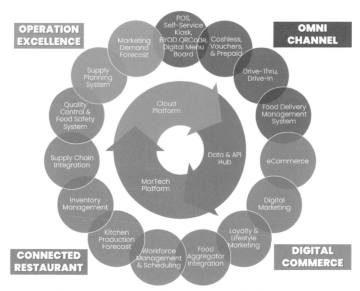

State-of-the-Art RestTech Ecosystem Architecture.

Point of Sales System (POS)

The Point of Sale (POS) system in a QSR is a central technology hub within a restaurant that plays a crucial role in various aspects of restaurant operations. Here's a breakdown of its key functions and significance:

1. **Order Processing**
   The POS system is the hub for order processing. It allows staff to input customer orders, customize them according to preferences, and specify any modifications. This ensures that orders are accurate and meet customer expectations.

2. **Payment Processing**
   The POS system handles payments, including cash, credit/debit cards, mobile wallets, and gift cards. It calculates totals, applies discounts, and generates receipts, facilitating efficient and secure transactions.

3. **Menu and Pricing Management**
   QSRs frequently update their menus with promotions, limited time offers (LTOs), seasonal items, or changes in pricing. The POS system allows for easy menu and pricing adjustments, ensuring that customers see the correct items and prices when ordering.

4. **Sales Reporting and Analytics**
   POS systems generate detailed sales reports and analytics. QSR owners and managers can access information on sales trends, peak hours, popular menu items, and more. This data guides business decisions, such as menu optimizations and marketing strategies.

5. **Customer Loyalty Programs**
   Some POS systems integrate with customer loyalty programs, allowing customers to earn rewards or points for their purchases. This encourages repeat business and strengthens customer relationships.

6. **Integration with Other Technologies**

   POS systems can integrate with various other technologies in a QSR, such as self-service kiosks, mobile apps, food aggregator marketplaces, and kitchen display systems, ensuring seamless communication between different channels of the business.

A typical touchscreen POS system for capturing customer orders. (Credit: Posiflex)

Restaurant Point of Sales system with a customer-facing screen to display order details. It also up-sells new products with promotional items. A good POS system needs to be integrated with features such as a cashless payment terminal, receipt printer, and NFC and QR Code scanner.
(Credit: McDonald's UAE)

Tablet-type POS is a popular choice for modern QSR with a complex made-to-order menu structure. (Credit: Taco Bell China)

The Simphony POS system from Oracle is built for complete restaurant management. The tablet POS companion is best suited for restaurant format with casual dining and table-side ordering settings. (Source: www.oracle.com)

Ultra-modern HP ElitePOS with integrated receipt printer suitable for long hours of operation with minimal fatigue. (Credit: HP)

A new generation of cloud POS solutions that empowers QSR Omnichannel business. (Source: www.xilnex.com)

In summary, the POS system is the nerve center of QSR's operations, managing everything from order processing and payment handling to data analytics. It streamlines processes, enhances accuracy, and provides valuable insights that help QSRs optimize their offerings and improve customer experiences.

Self-Service Kiosks

Self-service kiosks play a pivotal role in QSRs by providing an efficient and customer-centric ordering experience. These kiosks enable customers to independently place and customize their orders, make payments, and select preferences like toppings or sides.

This RestTech component offers several benefits:

1. **Enhanced Efficiency**
   Self-service kiosks reduce order processing times, minimizing wait times for customers, and enhancing overall service speed.
2. **Order Accuracy**
   Customers can customize orders precisely, reducing the likelihood of errors, and ensuring they receive their desired meals.
3. **Personalization**
   Kiosks can suggest add-ons or promotions based on customer choices, driving upsells and enhancing the customer experience.
4. **Upsell Opportunities**
   Through suggestive selling and visually appealing menus, kiosks encourage customers to explore additional items or upgrades.
5. **Reduced Labor Costs**
   While maintaining staff for essential roles, QSRs can allocate fewer resources to order-taking, optimizing labor efficiency.
6. **Data Collection**
   Kiosks collect valuable customer data, including ordering habits, which can be used to shape menu offerings and marketing strategies.
7. **Accessibility**

They cater to customers who prefer a digital interface and can accommodate various languages and accessibility needs.

8. **Social Distancing**

Particularly relevant in recent times, self-service kiosks support contactless ordering and payment, promoting safety.

A welcoming customer self-serving ordering kiosk with integrated digital payment system. With AI built-in to upsize and upsell to customers. (Credit: Burger King Scotland)

When Kiosks are placed at strategic locations, it helps to create brand awareness and invite customers to order, even if the restaurant is located perhaps in the hidden real-estate corner. (Credit: McDonald's Malaysia)

*In KFC China, kiosks complemented with QR Code and mobile app integration
for seamless customer experience and loyalty application. (Credit: KFC China)*

A tabletop version of the kiosk projects a more modern contemporary look.
(Credit: Taco Bell)

Kiosks are a fit-for-purpose solution that allows staff to focus on food preparation and customer service tasks while ensuring customers can place orders quickly and effectively. (Source: http://fingermark.ai)

Kiosks being evaluated in a digital lab come in different designs, sizes, and features. QSR operators must evaluate them with their physical constraints in the restaurant environment.

Kiosks have different specifications and run on different operating software such as Windows IoT or Android. It has embedded devices like a receipt printer, cashless terminal, and QRCode scanner (Credit: Longbow Kiosks).

From our practical point of view, self-service kiosks lead to reduced restaurant headcount by 1.5 to 2 full-time equivalents (FTE). At the same time, the AI upsell and upsize engine of the kiosk can increase the ticket average by about 6%.

In summary, self-service kiosks are integral to QSRs, modernizing operations, enhancing order accuracy, personalizing the customer experience, and facilitating customer data acquisition. Moving into the future, these will be the key digital touchpoints for customers.

BYOD QR Code Order Channel

Also known as Bring Your Own Device (BYOD), this is a contactless ordering channel where a QR code is the ordering channel where a QSR allows customers to access menus, place orders, and make payments using their smart devices. In most cases, by scanning a QR code generated and displayed in the restaurant or on promotional materials, customers can enjoy a contactless and convenient ordering experience. This technology minimizes physical contact, reduces the need for lining up, and enhances order accuracy, aligning with modern preferences for efficiency and safety in dining. This channel allows QSRs to identify their customers and be able to use order history to present a personalized menu and upsell featured or relevant items accordingly.

Lazy to queue up, now you can order KFC without leaving your table. (Credit: KFC Malaysia)

BYOD QRCode self-ordering channel provides unparalleled convenience for customers to place orders right from the dining table and skip queue. (Credit: KFC China)

BYOD Channel that has built-in AI for upselling. (Credit: Pizza Hut Malaysia)

In summary, QR code ordering is a technology-driven channel that enhances the customer experience, streamlines operations, and offers a contactless solution, which has become especially important in the context of the COVID-19 pandemic. It provides convenience, accuracy, and data-driven insights that enable QSRs to better serve their customers and stay competitive amidst a rapidly evolving industry.

Digital Menu Display (DMB)

Also known as Signage Display Boards, these are normally what customers look at the moment they walk into a QSR restaurant. Digital menu displays are an integral component of QSRs in the modern dining landscape as their role extends beyond merely listing menu items; they serve as dynamic tools for facilitating customer engagement, enhancing ordering efficiency, and adapting to the evolving expectations of diners.

Here's a breakdown of their multifaceted role:

1. **Engaging Visual Presentation**
   Digital menu displays utilize vibrant visuals, enticing images, and animations to present menu items in an engaging and visually appealing manner. This captivates customers, making menu exploration more enticing and enjoyable.

2. **Promotions, Upsizing and Upselling**
   Digital displays can strategically highlight promotions, combos, and add-ons, increasing the average transaction value. They can also suggest complementary items, driving upselling and upsizing opportunities.

3. **Real-time Updates**
   Digital displays enable QSRs to update menus in real time. This flexibility is invaluable for showcasing daily specials, limited-time promotions, and menu changes swiftly, ensuring that customers always see the latest offerings.

4. **Dynamic Menu Customization**
   These displays often support customization options, allowing operators to tailor their menus based on the situational data. For example, they can easily update menu items depending on parameters such as local weather conditions, festivities, etc. This personalization not only enhances the customer experience but also drives upselling.

5. **Order Accuracy**

Clear, detailed item descriptions and visuals reduce the likelihood of order errors. Customers can easily verify their selections or in some cases non-verbal communication such as pointing will be possible, leading to greater order accuracy.

6. **Dayparting**

QSRs can schedule menu changes based on the time of day. For instance, breakfast items can be prominently displayed during morning hours, and lunch or dinner options can take the spotlight at their respective times.

7. **Cost and Waste Reduction**

Digital menu displays eliminate the need for printing and distributing physical menus, reducing paper waste and associated costs to distribute them to each outlet. They are also more durable and require less maintenance than traditional menu boards.

8. **Enhanced Branding**

Consistent branding and messaging can be maintained across all locations with centralized control of digital displays. This ensures that the brand's image is portrayed consistently to customers.

9. **Nutritional Information**

QSRs can include nutritional information and calorie counts on digital displays, addressing customer demands for transparency and helping individuals make informed choices.

10. **Operational Efficiency**

These displays can integrate with POS systems, streamlining the ordering process and ensuring that orders placed at the display are accurately transmitted to the kitchen.

A well-designed digital menu board with upsizing and upselling features.
(Credit: KFC China)

A digital menu board complementing the kiosks in a contemporary design.
(Credit: KFC Malaysia)

A diverse DMB that not only shows the core menu items, it also shows the promotional items and add-on items for upselling.
(Credit: McDonald's Malaysia)

A diverse DMB can be vertically oriented to address the space limitations of the storefront. (Credit: McDonald's Ireland)

In summary, digital menu displays are versatile tools that carry functionalities that are far beyond capabilities of the static menu boards. They serve as dynamic platforms for engaging customers, promoting menu items, personalizing orders, and enhancing operational efficiency. In an era of evolving customer expectations and digital convenience, these displays are essential for QSRs seeking to remain competitive and deliver exceptional dining experiences.

Cashless Payment Convenient

Cashless payment systems have revolutionized the way QSRs operate and serve customers. These digital payment methods play a pivotal role in enhancing convenience, speed, and security in QSRs. Here's a breakdown of their role:

1. **Speed and Efficiency**
   Cashless payments, such as credit/debit cards, mobile wallets, and digital payment apps, expedite the checkout process. Customers can complete payment transactions swiftly, reducing wait times and enhancing overall service speed.

2. **Contactless Transactions**
   In an era marked by health and safety concerns, contactless payment methods offer customers a secure and touch-free way to make purchases. This minimizes the risk of germ/viral transmissions and adheres to health guidelines.

3. **Convenience**
   Cashless payment systems provide customers with flexibility and convenience. They can pay using their preferred methods, whether it's a physical card, an E-Wallet, a mobile app, or wearable technology.

4. **Order Accuracy**
   Digital payments are often integrated with Point of Sale (POS) systems, reducing the chances of errors in processing payments and ensuring that transactions are accurately recorded.

5. **Multiple Payment Options**
   QSRs can accommodate a wide range of payment methods, catering to diverse customer preferences. This inclusivity helps maximize customer satisfaction.

6. **Integration with Loyalty Programs**

Many cashless payment systems are integrated with loyalty programs or rewards schemes. This encourages repeat business and strengthens customer loyalty.

7. **Reduced Cash Handling**

   QSRs can minimize the need for cash handling, which can be logistically challenging, time-consuming, and susceptible to errors or theft.

8. **Security**

   Cashless payments offer a higher level of security. They are protected by encryption and authentication measures, reducing the risk of theft or fraud associated with handling physical cash.

9. **Data Insights**

   QSRs can gather valuable transaction data through cashless payment systems. This data can be used for analytics, helping businesses understand customer behavior and preferences, and guiding marketing strategies.

10. **Operational Efficiency**

    Cashless payments simplify accounting and reporting processes. Transaction records are easily accessible and can be seamlessly integrated into other financial systems.

11. **Adaptability to Trends**

    Cashless payment systems can adapt to emerging trends, including mobile payments, QR code payments, and digital wallets. This keeps QSRs aligned with evolving customer preferences.

Cashless payment convenience needs to be in all channels.
(Credit: KFC China & KFC Malaysia)

In summary, cashless payment systems are instrumental in QSRs for their role in expediting transactions, enhancing customer convenience, and promoting security. Their adaptability to diverse payment methods and integration with loyalty programs make them essential tools for improving customer experiences and operational efficiency in modern QSRs.

Best Practices!

It's always recommended to have a clean front counter policy where POS are neatly set up. One single cashless terminal to be connected to capture various payment instruments and vouchers. The cashless terminal needs to be able to read credit cards, NFC, QRCode, E-Wallet, Samsung Pay, and Apple Pay. Providing frictionless convenience to customers. Notably, there are QSR operators who made mistakes by having many different terminals for different payment instruments. This adds confusion to customers, and staff crews and increases tech support overheads.

Drive Thru Channel

In the morning and evening rush hours, you often see queues in the restaurant drive-through. Drive-Thru tends to accommodate customers who are busy commuting to/from work. The drive-thru channel is a vital component of its customer service strategy. It offers a convenient and efficient way for customers to order and receive their meals without leaving their vehicles.

In terms of implementation, generally, a menu board and voice ordering system at the drive-thru ordering point are key to customer touchpoints. In the kitchen, there is a need for a pick-by-voice system for the kitchen crew to pack food as it is being ordered. In addition, traffic monitoring and control within the drive-thru lane is essential.

Here's a concise description of its key role:

1. **Streamlined Convenience**
   The drive-thru channel streamlines the entire dining process, from ordering to payment and food pickup. Customers can quickly place their orders, make payments, and receive their meals, reducing wait times and enhancing convenience.

2. **Contactless Service**
   Especially relevant in recent times, the drive-thru provides a contactless dining option, minimizing physical interactions and promoting safety for both customers and staff.

3. **Efficient Operations**
   QSRs optimize their drive-thru operations to handle high volumes of orders efficiently. This includes well-trained staff, digital menu boards, and synchronized order processing systems, ensuring speedy and accurate service.

4. **Customer Preferences**
   The drive-thru caters to customer preferences for on-the-go dining. It's particularly popular for breakfast and lunch, making it a significant revenue generator for QSRs.

5. **Flexibility**

   Drive-thru channels often accommodate mobile app orders and promotions, further enhancing the customer experience and fostering loyalty.

Drive-thru implementation with a customer order display with a voice ordering system. (Credit: KFC Malaysia)

QSR's drive-thru digital channel enables a super-efficient experience for customers through voice ordering and kitchen voice-picking solutions right from their car. (Credit: KFC Malaysia)

The innovative multi-lane drive-through store further enhances the customer experience during peak hours. This is particularly effective in high-volume drive-thru markets. (Credit: KFC Australia)

A typical QSR drive-thru system implementation using technology as offered by Oracle. (Source: www.oracle.com)

In summary, the drive-thru channel is an integral part of QSR's strategy, offering speed, convenience, and safety for customers while contributing significantly to the restaurant's operational efficiency and revenue stream.

Online Ordering Channels

With the widespread popularity of the Internet, people tend to be connected anywhere and anytime. Capitalizing on this phenomenon, QSRs need to be accessible right on the spot to catch their craving. The online ordering channel serves as a digital platform that allows customers to place orders and make payments online. It provides a convenient and contactless way for customers to access the QSR's menu, customize orders, and arrange for delivery or pickup regardless of their current location. These e-commerce channels streamline ordering processes, enhance customer convenience, and enable QSRs to reach a broader audience, expanding their market reach beyond traditional dine-in customers. This digital channel aligns with modern consumer preferences for online transactions and complements in-store and drive-thru experiences.

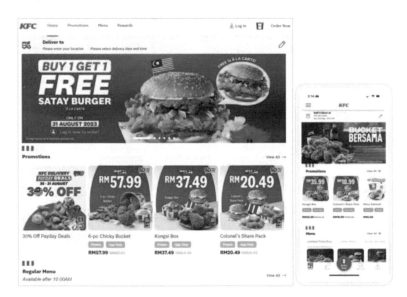

Online ordering channels allow customers to place orders and deliver to their doorstep or self-collect from the restaurant. (Credit: KFC Malaysia)

Mobile Apps - The Pocket-Sized Restaurants

In addition, mobile apps have indeed transformed the restaurant industry by offering a pocket-sized solution for both customers and restaurant owners. These apps provide a wide range of functionalities, making dining experiences more convenient, efficient, and enjoyable. Here are some key aspects of mobile apps as "pocket-sized restaurants":

1. **Online Ordering and Delivery**
    Mobile apps enable customers to engage with restaurants, starting from browsing restaurant menus and placing orders, up until having the food delivered to their doorstep.

2. **Reservations**
    Many restaurants now offer reservation features in their apps. Customers can book tables in advance, reducing wait times and ensuring a seamless dining experience.

3. **Menu Exploration**
    Mobile apps often include detailed menus with descriptions, prices, and images of dishes. This helps customers in making informed choices and discover new items they might not have tried otherwise.

4. **Customization and Special Requests**
    Apps allow customers to customize their orders and make special requests, such as dietary preferences or extra toppings. This level of personalization enhances the dining experience.

5. **Payment Options**
    Mobile apps usually offer various payment methods, including credit/debit cards, digital wallets (e.g., Apple Pay, Google Pay), and even in-app loyalty points redemption.

6. **Loyalty Programs**

Many restaurant apps have loyalty programs that reward customers with points or discounts for frequent orders. This incentivizes customer loyalty.

7. **Feedback and Ratings**

Customers can provide feedback and ratings directly through the app, helping restaurants improve their services and allowing others to make informed decisions about where to dine.

8. **Push Notifications**

Restaurants can send notifications about special offers, new menu items, or upcoming events, keeping customers engaged and informed.

9. **Food Tracking**

Apps with food delivery services often include real-time tracking, allowing customers to monitor the status of their orders from the restaurant to their doorstep.

10. **Online Payment**

In some upscale restaurants, mobile apps facilitate online payment, reducing the need for physical bills and cash transactions.

11. **Contactless**

Post-COVID-19 pandemic, mobile apps have also played a crucial role in ensuring health and safety. They can display COVID-19 guidelines, offer contactless payment options, and even provide QR codes for digital menus.

12. **Integration with Third-party Services**

Restaurants can integrate their apps with third-party services like social media, online review platforms, and analytic tools to better understand their customers and market their business effectively.

Mobile apps enable brand accessibility in your pocket in the modern world.
(Credit: McDonald's Malaysia)

Mobile apps have revolutionized the restaurant industry, transforming the customers' experience of interacting with restaurants where they can essentially get the products without going physically near any F&B outlets and instead solely interacting with their mobile devices. As technology continues to evolve, these "pocket-sized restaurants" are likely to offer even more features and innovations in the future.

Food Aggregator Channels

Food aggregators such as Uber Eats, FoodPanda, Grab, Deliveroo, Zomato, and Food Hub play a crucial role in QSRs by acting as intermediaries between these establishments and their customers. Their marketplace platforms provide an online channel where QSRs can list their menu items, and customers can browse, order, and pay for food. Food aggregators facilitate food delivery, offering an additional revenue stream and increasing QSR's visibility. They streamline the ordering process, provide access to a broader customer base, and handle logistics, making them essential partners for QSRs looking to expand their reach and offer convenient delivery services, especially smaller brands that are unable to invest in their marketing, delivery services, and in some cases capacity for seating customers.

To be efficient, QSR operators need to integrate these marketplaces into their commerce engine and be able to seamlessly capture the orders into their POS and kitchen system.

QSR needs to leverage food aggregators' marketplaces to widen their brand reach and sales.
(Credit: Grab Malaysia)

Gojek's GoFood is a big success in Indonesia. (Credit: Gojek)

In addition, food aggregators are providing last-mile food delivery services, enhancing restaurant's coverage. (Credit: Uber Eats)

Food aggregators help QSR in generating additional sales but take away margins.

Chapter 3:
Operational Challenges and RestTech Solutions

In this chapter, we'll delve deeper into the Omnichannel Experience, exploring how large-scale QSR brands are leveraging technology to seamlessly connect with customers across various touchpoints. From mobile apps to self-service kiosks, discover how the dining journey has evolved into an interconnected web of digital and physical interactions.

The QSR industry is not without its challenges. However, digital solutions have emerged as powerful tools to overcome these hurdles and transform QSR operations. In this section, we'll explore some common challenges faced by QSRs and how digital technologies can help address them effectively.

Challenges and RestTech Solutions

The following highlights challenges faced by QSR operators and how digital solutions can address the challenges.

1. **High Demand and Peak Times**
   Challenge: Managing high customer traffic during peak hours can lead to long wait times, order errors, and consequently decreased customer satisfaction. Often, the Speed of Service (SoS) KPIs of QSR operator suffers.
   Digital Solution: Digital order-taking systems, self-service kiosks, and mobile apps enable customers to place orders and make payments quickly. These solutions reduce congestion, enhance order accuracy, and streamline the order   process.

2. **Inability of Restaurant Crew to Upsize and Upsell Customer Orders**

Challenge: Due to a lack of training or being under pressure when there are long customer queues, restaurant crews tend to skip the upsize and upsell stage of the customer order-taking process, leading to missing potential revenue.

Digital Solution: With digital self-ordering. Customers scroll through the digital menu and place their orders at their own pace. At the same time, being able to upsize their Coke to a large cup and AI engine within the digital platform can recommend a dessert to customers to complete their meal.

3. **Inventory Management**

Challenge: Balancing inventory levels to avoid shortages while minimizing waste is a constant challenge.

Digital Solution: Data-driven inventory management systems utilize real-time data to monitor ingredient levels, track consumption patterns, and automate reordering. This ensures optimal inventory levels and reduces food waste.

4. **Employee Training and Efficiency**

Challenge: High turnover rates and the need for consistent training can impact service quality and operational efficiency.

Digital Solution: Digital training modules and e-learning platforms provide standardized training for employees. Digital scheduling systems optimize staffing levels based on historical data and peak hours, ensuring efficient resource allocation.

5. **Customer Engagement and Personalization**
   Challenge: Engaging customers beyond the physical restaurant can be difficult, leading to decreased brand loyalty.
   Digital Solution: Customer relationship management (CRM) systems and loyalty programs integrated with mobile apps gather data on customer preferences and behaviors. This data enables personalized promotions, discounts, and rewards, fostering brand loyalty.

6. **Order Accuracy and Communication**
   Challenge: Miscommunication between front-of-house and kitchen staff can result in incorrect orders and customer dissatisfaction.
   Digital Solution: Digital kitchen display systems connected to order-taking devices ensure accurate communication between staff members. This minimizes errors and improves order accuracy.

7. **Marketing and Promotion Efficiency**
   Challenge: Traditional marketing methods may not reach tech-savvy customers effectively.
   Digital Solution: Digital marketing platforms allow QSRs to create targeted campaigns based on customer data. Social media, email marketing, and mobile apps provide avenues for promoting offers and engaging customers directly.

8. **Menu Innovation and Adaptability**
   Challenge: Adapting menus to changing consumer preferences and introducing new items can be time-consuming and resource intensive.
   Digital Solution: Digital menu boards enable QSRs to update menus remotely and in real-time. This flexibility allows for rapid menu changes, seasonal offerings, and

dynamic   promotions.

9. **Data Security and Privacy**
    Challenge: Collecting and storing customer data while ensuring security and compliance with regulations can be complex.
    Digital Solution: Implementing robust data security measures, encryption, and compliance with data protection laws ensures that customer information is safeguarded while allowing for personalized experiences.

10. **Feedback and Continuous Improvement**
    Challenge: Gathering customer feedback and acting on it in a timely manner can be challenging.
    Digital Solution: Digital feedback platforms enable customers to provide real-time feedback via apps or QR codes. This data informs operational improvements and helps address issues promptly.

By embracing digital solutions tailored to address these challenges, QSRs can further optimize their operations, enhance customer experiences, and position themselves for success in an ever-evolving landscape. The integration of digital technologies ensures that QSRs can not only meet but also exceed customer expectations, creating a win-win scenario for both customers and the QSR business.

Chapter 4:
The Power of Omnichannel Experience

In the modern QSR landscape, the dining journey is no longer confined to the walls of a physical restaurant. The omnichannel experience has emerged as a game changer, enabling QSR brands to engage with customers in diverse and dynamic ways. This chapter explores the multi-faceted world of omnichannel interactions and how they redefine customer engagement.

Omnichannel in action, providing options for customers to transact with the brands. (Credit: McDonald's Singapore).

The Seamless Convergence of Physical and Digital Spaces

Nowadays, consumers are shying away from queuing for goods. In the realm of modern QSRs, the lines between physical and digital spaces are blurring, giving rise to a seamless and dynamic dining experience. This convergence, facilitated by RestTech, is reshaping the way QSRs operate and engage with their customers.

RestTech has redefined the physical space of QSRs. The traditional dine-in experience is evolving to accommodate digital touchpoints. Self-service kiosks and mobile ordering apps allow customers to interact with menus, place orders, and make payments seamlessly. These digital interfaces seamlessly merge with the physical restaurant environment, reducing wait times and enhancing convenience.

RestTech further extends the QSR experience beyond physical space. Online ordering, delivery, and curbside pickup options have become integral components of QSRs' digital strategies. Customers can access menus, place orders, and receive meals from the comfort of their homes or vehicles, blurring the boundaries between physical and digital dining experiences.

On the same note, data-driven personalization further bridges these spaces. Customer preferences and behaviors are collected through digital interactions which helps to better tailor promotions and recommendations, whether customers are dining in, ordering online, or opting for delivery.

QSR brands with a clear RestTech strategy are orchestrating a seamless convergence of physical and digital spaces in the QSR landscape. This synergy enhances convenience, personalization, and accessibility, ensuring that QSRs remain at the forefront of the evolving dining landscape and cater effectively to the preferences of modern consumers.

Online Ordering and Delivery Platforms

The QSR industry has witnessed a transformative shift in its operations with the rapid rise of online ordering and delivery services. From a RestTech implementation standpoint, this evolution represents a strategic pivot to meet evolving consumer preferences and market demands.

QSR brands have embraced third-party delivery partnerships and developed their delivery apps, recognizing that convenience is paramount for modern consumers. RestTech tools such as mobile devices or online ordering platforms play a pivotal role in making this transition seamless.

Digital storefronts and mobile apps provide customers with user-friendly interfaces to place orders and track deliveries. These platforms integrate with POS and kitchen management systems, ensuring efficient order processing and accurate delivery coordination.

Data-driven insights gleaned from RestTech empower QSRs to optimize their delivery strategies. They can analyze heatmaps, order patterns, delivery times, and customer preferences to enhance efficiency and tailor promotions.

RestTech also facilitates secure and contactless payment options, aligning with today's safety-conscious consumers. This enhances the overall customer experience while ensuring transaction security.

QSRs need to embrace online ordering and delivery services as a strategic move to leverage technology for convenience and business coverage expansion. RestTech's role in streamlining order processing, enhancing data-driven decision-making, and ensuring secure transactions positions QSRs for success in this increasingly digital dining landscape.

Self-Service Kiosks-The Forefront of Restaurant Transformation

While QSRs are experiencing an in-store digital revolution, self-service kiosks stand at the forefront of this transformation. These interactive screens are not just tools for streamlining operations; they are empowering customers' freedom of brand interaction as well as being integral to QSRs' omnichannel digital strategies.

Firstly, self-service kiosks put ordering power directly into the hands of customers. Customers need to identify themselves, then browse menus, customize their orders, and even pay at their own pace. This level of control enhances the overall dining experience by reducing wait times and ensuring order accuracy.

Secondly, they facilitate a seamless omnichannel experience. Orders placed through kiosks seamlessly integrate with the POS system and kitchen management system. This consistency allows customers to enjoy a frictionless ordering experience.

Furthermore, self-service kiosks support personalization. They can suggest add-ons, upsells, or promotions based on customer choices, improving the average transaction value, and driving revenue uplift.

In essence, self-service kiosks are not just digital gadgets; they are the embodiment of QSRs' commitment to customer-centricity. They empower customers with choice, convenience, and personalization, making them pivotal in a successful omnichannel digital strategy that elevates customer satisfaction and fosters loyalty.

Kiosks are effective customers' digital touchpoints. (Credit: KFC Malaysia)

KFC kiosks can be brand ambassadors, making the QSR brand vibrant and young. (Credit: KFC China)

In-Store Technology That Enhancing the Dine-In Experience

RestTech innovations not only optimize operations but also elevate the frictionless customer experience.

Self-service kiosks are a prime example. These interactive screens empower customers to browse menus, customize orders, and make payments effortlessly. This not only reduces wait times but also minimizes order errors, ensuring a smooth and accurate dining experience.

Furthermore, digital menu board displays offer dynamic visuals and real-time updates, enabling QSRs to showcase dayparts, promotions, and specials seamlessly. This captures customer attention and drives upsell.

BYOD, another RestTech component enables customers to place orders, request refills, or even pay without having to flag down a server. This promotes efficiency and convenience.

In conclusion, RestTech is enhancing the dine-in experience in QSRs by offering convenience, personalization, and efficiency. By thoughtfully integrating these technologies, QSRs not only streamline their operations but also create a dining environment that caters to modern customer expectations, solidifying their position in a competitive market.

Kiosks with digital menu boards as backdrop enhance customer ordering experience. (Credit: McDonald's Ireland)

Best Practices!

While RestTech can enhance efficiency and convenience in QSRs, it can't fully replace the human touches of the brand experience. Customers seek personal interactions, empathy, and the ability to address unique requests. The actual restaurant staff provides warmth, problem-solving, and the personal touch that technology lacks. They create emotional connections that are crucial for customer loyalty and the overall QSR experience. Technology can support, but not entirely replace, these human interactions from the customer's perspective.

Chapter 5:
Revolutionizing E-commerce Integration

As we speak, the world's consumers are increasingly gravitating toward going online to make purchases from food aggregator platforms. In this context, e-commerce Integration has become the cornerstone of QSR brands' success. This chapter explores how QSR giants are leveraging e-commerce platforms to transform the customer experience, streamline operations, and unlock new avenues for growth.

The Digital Storefront and Reimagining Ordering and Payment

This section delves into the concept of the digital storefront—a virtual gateway that allows customers to explore menus, customize orders, and make payments from the comfort of their devices. We explore the power of visual menus, allergen information, and secure payment gateways in enhancing the online ordering process.

In the ever-evolving landscape of QSRs, the digital storefront has emerged as a transformative force. It reinvents the way customers interact with QSRs, enhancing convenience, efficiency, and the overall dining experience.

1. **Convenient Ordering**
   The digital storefront offers customers the flexibility to browse menus, customize orders, and place them seamlessly via mobile apps or websites. This empowers patrons to skip long lines, reduce wait times, and tailor their meals to perfection.

2. **Contactless Transactions**
   In an era where health and safety are prioritized, the digital storefront provides a touchless solution. Customers can make cashless payments, reducing the need for physical currency exchange and minimizing contact with surfaces.

3. **Real-time Updates**
   QSRs can update their digital menus in real-time, ensuring that customers always see the latest offerings, prices, and promotions. This adaptability caters to evolving customer preferences and seasonal changes.

4. **Personalization**
   The digital storefront leverages data insights to offer personalized recommendations and promotions based on customer preferences and previous orders, enriching the dining experience, and driving customer loyalty.

5. **Operational Efficiency**
   Integrated with Point of Sale (POS) systems, the digital storefront streamlines order processing, minimizes errors, and optimizes inventory management. This operational efficiency improves both customers' experiences and QSRs' back-end operational efficiency.

Delivery Platforms for Expanding Reach and Convenience

There is a need to embrace delivery platforms as a necessary convenience for customers. The food delivery management system is the core of the restaurant BOH, enabling restaurant operators to manage and track their order fulfillment status, delivering food on time for customers every time. As a force multiplier of QSRs market penetration, this will be a necessary investment for QSRs.

Digital Loyalty Programs

The customer relationship of any restaurant business is driven by the restaurant staff. For instance, when a regular customer walks into the restaurant, he/she will be recognized by the staff, who will be putting up a smile and greeting them by their name. The staff will further recall their regular favorites and offer these defaults to the customer. This traditional customer-restaurant bond only persists if the customer visits the same restaurant or meets the same staff. However, the bonding elements will be missing if the same customer is visiting a different outlet or being serviced by another staff member.

Revamping traditional loyalty programs through digital channels, such as greeting customers by their names, knowing their favorites, and their birthdays when the mobile app is launched.

Additionally, the app tracks reward points and personalized offers based on customer preferences and behaviors. These programs enhance engagement, foster repeat business, and offer valuable data insights.

Starbucks app that greets customers by their names, with loyalty and pre-paid features. (Credit: Starbucks Malaysia)

MyMcDonald's Rewards. A super easy-to-use loyalty program was introduced by McDonald's. (Credit: McDonald's US)

Curbside Pickup and Contactless Experiences

As an added convenience to customers, QSR should explore contactless technologies and offer curbside pickup options. Implementing geolocation services, real-time order tracking, and QR code scanning to minimize physical contact, maximize peace of mind, and enhance the safety of both customers and staff.

Food Aggregator App

As part of the larger e-Commerce strategy, it is wise for QSR to consider partnerships with food aggregators services that have gained popularity as they provide a vast selection of restaurants and cuisines. Although they take away certain profit margins, they do help in generating incremental revenue. Aggregators also help in extending the delivery network coverage as well as increasing rider or delivery capacity that is often limited. However, QSR's RestTech will need to have an open API platform to be able to integrate their POS system with all the aggregators that they partner with to achieve maximum efficiency.

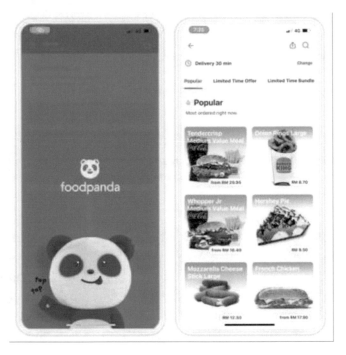

Extending QSR's brand reach through food aggregators' apps.
(Credit: FoodPanda)

Chapter 6:
Mastering the Back-of-the-House

This chapter immerses us in the heart of QSR operations, the Back-of-the-House, also known as BOH, which is a term used for all the behind-the-scenes action that customers typically don't have access to. This usually includes the kitchen, where the food is prepped and cooked as well as inventories and employee workspaces.

We'll explore how advanced kitchen systems, automation, and real-time data synchronization are revolutionizing the way QSRs prepare and deliver their offerings, ensuring consistency, speed, and quality.

In the realm of QSRs, the kitchen is where culinary artistry meets precision and efficiency. This chapter delves into the inner workings of the modern QSR kitchen, exploring advanced kitchen systems, automation, and real-time data synchronization that are reshaping the way QSRs prepare and deliver their offerings.

The Kitchen's Role in Customer Satisfaction
In the world of QSRs, the front-of-house is the pretty face of the brand, while the quality of the food served is the core substance of the business. The kitchen plays an equally pivotal role in shaping the dining experience and leaving a lasting impression on customers. This is precisely where RestTech comes to the forefront.

Firstly, RestTech enhances order accuracy using digital systems and kitchen display screens (KDS) to ensure that every order is prepared precisely to customer specifications. This minimizes errors and elevates customer satisfaction.

Secondly, RestTech optimizes kitchen workflows with automated processes, such as order routing and ingredient tracking, streamlining kitchen operations, reducing wait times, and ensuring faster service, which is crucial for QSRs.

Furthermore, data-driven insights generated by RestTech shed visibility on kitchen efficiency. QSRs can identify hot menu items, track ingredient usage, and adapt their kitchen prep accordingly.

Finally, RestTech supports real-time communication between front-of-house staff and kitchen teams. This coordination through the kitchen display screen ensures that orders are prepared promptly and accurately, even during chaotic peak hours.

In summary, RestTech empowers QSR kitchens to be the epicenter of customer satisfaction. By improving accuracy and efficiency, it ensures that every dish served is a testament to culinary excellence, leaving customers delighted and loyal.

NCR Aloha Point of Sales Solution that is integrated with the Aloha Kitchen system. (Source: www.ncr.com)

An effective kitchen display system can significantly improve the accuracy and efficiency of the kitchen. (Source: www.ncr.com)

An integrated Oracle MICROS Kitchen Display System that helps the front counter to communicate customer orders to the back of the house in real-time. A bump bar provided allows kitchen staff to update on the food preparation status. Thus, improving the overall order cycle and speed of service management. (Credit: Oracle)

Order Automation from Customer to Kitchen

Order automation from customer to kitchen refers to seamlessly connecting the customer's order to the kitchen, reducing wait times, enhancing accuracy, and optimizing operations. From self-service kiosks or mobile apps, orders flow directly to the kitchen display systems, triggering efficient food preparation. This streamlining of the process ensures that every customer's order is handled swiftly and accurately, leading to improved customer satisfaction and operational efficiency—evidence of the transformative power of RestTech in modernizing QSR operations.

Application Programming Interfaces (APIs) play a crucial role in facilitating seamless communication between various software systems. They enable real-time data exchange, allowing orders from digital channels like mobile apps or self-service kiosks to flow effortlessly into kitchen systems. Eliminating the redundancy of order entry by the staff, APIs ensure smooth order automation, reducing errors and enhancing efficiency, ultimately elevating the staff efficiency.

Kitchen and order status displays are key to managing the anxiety of customers when waiting for the food.

83

Inventory Management System

Inventory management is another core of the restaurant BOH function. It is also key for real-time synchronization of critical raw ingredients from their restaurants to their supply chain centers. It ensures that restaurants have the right ingredients at the right time, reducing waste, controlling costs, and ensuring menu availability. RestTech's data-driven inventory management systems offer real-time insights, enabling predictive ordering, automatic alerts for restocking, and streamlined supplier relations. This not only optimizes operations but also enhances customer satisfaction by guaranteeing availability, and undisrupted menu offerings. In the dynamic QSR industry, effective inventory management through RestTech is the key to achieving operational excellence.

Inventory management is a massive core of restaurant managers from ordering, to ensuring sufficient stock and food costs management.

Using a cloud-based inventory management system changes the entire landscape of BOH administrative chores with the inventory controls in your pocket. (Credit: Food Market Hub)

Streamlining Food Preparation

This section highlights the technology that empowers kitchen staff to prepare food efficiently. From automated cooking projection systems, and timers to digital recipe displays, QSRs are embracing tools that streamline food preparation and maintain quality across the entire kitchen operations.

Efficiency is the cornerstone of a successful restaurant kitchen, where the delicate dance of preparing and serving dishes requires precision and speed. Streamlining food preparation is not just a matter of convenience; it can significantly impact a restaurant's profitability and customer satisfaction.

One key tool for streamlining is the use of technology. Modern kitchens employ various kitchen management software. Additionally, inventory management systems help monitor stock levels, minimizing wastage and cost.

The strategic organization of kitchen layouts, and the placement of digital devices, kitchen equipment, and food-holding cabinets can significantly reduce unnecessary movement and waiting times. This layout optimization minimizes the risk of bottlenecks during busy periods, allowing for smoother food preparation and quicker service.

The kitchen display system conveys demand projection data to the kitchen efficiently. (Credit: NCR Aloha Kitchen).

Quality Assurance and Food Safety

Food safety is a stringent requirement of any QSR brand, to ensure all regulatory requirements are adhered to. RestTech plays a crucial role in enhancing quality assurance and food safety within modern QSR kitchens.

Firstly, digital tools and software facilitate inventory management, ensuring that food products are stored and used within their shelf life. Automated tracking helps identify and remove expired items, reducing the risk of serving spoiled ingredients.

Secondly, temperature monitoring systems, often integrated with Internet of Things (IoT) devices, continuously track storage and cooking temperatures. Any deviations trigger immediate alerts, preventing the serving of undercooked or overcooked food, which can be both a safety hazard and a quality concern.

Thirdly, RestTech enables real-time traceability. In the event of a food safety incident or a quality issue, restaurants can quickly trace the origin of ingredients, helping to isolate and address the problem promptly.

Moreover, digital checklists and compliance management tools assist in maintaining hygiene and sanitation standards. These tools ensure that cleaning schedules are adhered to, preventing cross-contamination, and maintaining food safety.

Lastly, customer feedback and reviews, collected through digital platforms, provide valuable insights into food quality. Restaurants can use this data for continuous improvement and quality control.

Overall, RestTech enhances quality assurance and food safety in restaurants by automating processes, ensuring compliance, and facilitating real-time monitoring and traceability. These advancements not only prevent foodborne illnesses but also elevate the overall consumer confidence and dining experience, ultimately benefiting both customers and QSRs.

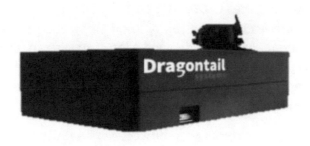

DragonTail System's QT Camera is an innovative imaging solution that scans any pizza that comes out of the oven, "grading" it based on pizza type, correct toppings, topping distribution, and other accuracy factors.
(Source: www.dragontail.com)

Digitalizing Restaurant Staff Training

As explored earlier, food safety, food preparation procedures, and recipe management demand a lot of training for BOH staff. Ensuring effective training and certification requires care planning and execution for QSRs with a massive network of restaurants.

The training and certification process can be digitalized with the help of RestTech. The deployment of eLearning apps helps field training teams to be able to put the training content online and can replace paper-bound types of training with online video, assessment, and certification.

In the event of future revisions to their materials, the staff can easily get the new materials digitally and do not require a field trainer to visit the restaurant branch to provide the training.

Chapter 7:
Crafting a Data Strategy for Success

This chapter dives into the realm of data strategy, revealing how QSRs harness BOH data to gain insights into operation efficiencies in the back of the house and then understand how data-driven decision-making can propel QSRs to new heights of success in a digital age.

Data is the currency that fuels intelligent decision-making and strategic growth. This chapter unveils the power of data in the QSR BOH landscape, exploring how leading brands are crafting robust data strategies to gain better kitchen, labor, inventory management, and supply chain efficiencies.

BOH Operational Optimization for Enhancing Efficiency

Data plays a pivotal role in enhancing operational efficiencies in the back of the house in several aspects:

1. **Omnichannel Menu Management**
   Data enables dynamic menu management. By analyzing customer order data, QSRs can identify popular items, seasonal trends, and underperforming dishes. This data-driven approach allows them to streamline raw material sourcing, eliminate low-demand items, and highlight bestsellers, improving efficiency and profitability.

2. **Supply Chain Optimization**
   Data can be used to optimize supply chains. It can provide real-time information on ingredient availability, consumption patterns, and vendor performance. This data-driven approach ensures that supply orders are timely,

reducing wastage and costs, and maintaining consistent food quality.

3. **Inventory Management**
Data can be leveraged for efficient inventory management. By monitoring real-time inventory levels and analyzing usage patterns, the Supply Chain Department can minimize over and understocking issues. This results in reduced food wastage and potential sales loss.

4. **Staff Scheduling**
Data-driven insights into sales patterns and customer foot traffic can help the Operation Department optimize staff scheduling. It ensures that the right number of employees are present during peak hours and can be scaled down during slower periods, thus optimizing labor costs.

Predictive Analytics

Predictive analytics is a powerful component of RestTech that empowers QSRs with better business insights. It involves utilizing transactional data, statistical algorithms, and machine learning techniques to forecast future trends, outcomes, and customer behaviors accurately.

Predictive analytics and machine learning models utilize data to anticipate customer behavior and trends. Predictive analytics makes future projections based on historical data, while machine learning models continuously learn from data to make real-time predictions, improving customer experiences, supply chain management, and decision-making. When put to good use, these can transform a QSR's kitchen into a Smart Kitchen that is super-efficient.

Predictive analytics has several applications:

1. **Demand Forecasting**
   By analyzing past sales data, weather patterns, and other factors, QSRs can predict future demand for specific menu items. This enables better inventory management, improves food costs, and reduces food waste. With RestTech, it is recommended that the predictive model be connected to Google Weather for instance. If the event of rain, the production forecast in the kitchen can be further optimized.

2. **Optimizing Operations**
   Predictive models can anticipate peak hours and busy periods, allowing QSRs to schedule staff accordingly. This ensures efficient service and optimizes labor costs.

3. **Supply Chain Management**
   Predictive analytics helps in predicting supply chain disruptions, ensuring a steady flow of ingredients, and minimizing disruptions that could affect sales. In other words, this will prevent unwanted inventory surprises from occurring during operating hours.

4. **Menu Development**
   QSRs can use predictive analytics to identify trending ingredients, flavors, and menu items. This data-driven approach can inspire menu development and innovation.

Furthermore, data-driven insights inform strategic decisions, from expanding to new restaurant locations to adapting menus to cater to changing consumer tastes. In an industry where speed and convenience are paramount, data-driven decision-making empowers QSRs to stay ahead of the competition, continuously improve, and remain agile in an ever-evolving market. Ultimately, the data-driven revolution is shaping QSRs into more customer-centric, efficient, and competitive brands.

Real-Time Analytics for Agile Decision-Making

Real-time analytics for decision-making

Real-time analytics in QSRs involves the instant collection, processing, and interpretation of data from various sources within the RestTech platforms. It empowers QSRs to harness data from their omnichannel to make agile, data-driven decisions aimed at maximizing sales and operational efficiency.

Real-time analytics provides insights into customer behavior, order trends, and inventory levels as they happen. For example, it can identify which menu items are selling well at a particular time of day or which promotions are resonating with customers. Armed with this information, the marketing team can swiftly adjust menus, pricing, and promotions to capitalize on emerging opportunities.

Chapter 8:
Building a Customer Data Platform (CDP)

Continuing the exploration of data, focusing on building a Customer Data Platform (CDP). Learn how leading QSR brands are harnessing CDPs to create a centralized repository of customer data, enabling personalized experiences, targeted marketing, and more.

In the age of digital transformation, the QSR industry is leveraging advanced technologies to better understand and serve its customers. This chapter delves into the concept of a CDP and how leading QSR brands are using this innovative solution to centralize customer data, drive personalization, and optimize costs while doing so.

Empowering Marketing with CDP

Centralized customer data is the backbone of a successful QSR's RestTech strategy. It refers to the aggregation and management of customer information from various touchpoints, such as POS, in-store kiosks, mobile apps, websites, in-store interactions, and loyalty programs, into a unified database.

This consolidated data offers several transformative advantages:

1. **Personalization**
   Centralized data allows QSRs to understand individual customer preferences, ordering habits, and demographics. Armed with this knowledge, they can provide tailored recommendations, offers, and experiences, enhancing customer satisfaction and repeat purchases.
2. **Loyalty Program**

CDP is the foundation of loyalty program implementations of QSRs. Knowing the details of customers captured in CDP, hasn't purchased enables personalized promotions, tailored rewards, and a seamless customer experience, fostering customer engagement and loyalty.

3. **Targeted Marketing**
   QSRs can segment their customer base effectively and deliver precisely targeted marketing campaigns. This ensures that promotions and communications resonate with specific customer groups, increasing the likelihood of successful conversion.

4. **Customer Retention**
   A CDP empowers brand marketing to enhance customer lifecycle management and reduce customer loss. It provides insights into their preferences and behaviors. When a customer hasn't purchased in the last three months, the CDP triggers personalized re-engagement campaigns. These can include targeted promotions, loyalty incentives, or new menu offerings. By reconnecting with lapsed customers, QSRs increase the likelihood of their return, effectively reducing customer loss and fostering long-term brand loyalty. On top of that, active customers can also be identified by CDP for improved purchase frequencies.

Enhancing Customer Experience with CDP

From a customer expectations perspective, we would assume that the brand would identify us by our name, favorite items, and even birthday. RestTech with CDP can be used to provide a highly individualized level of engagement for customers. The following are some of the key areas to highlight:

1. **Targeted Promotions**
   Through data analysis and AI processing, QSRs can send personalized promotions to customers' devices. These

targeted offers are not only more relevant but also more likely to drive sales and customer loyalty.

2. **Loyalty Programs**

   CDP enables sophisticated loyalty programs that reward customers for their engagement. Points, discounts, birthday vouchers, and exclusive offers are tailored to individual behavior, creating a sense of exclusivity and recognition.

3. **Predictive Ordering**

   Advanced algorithms can predict customer preferences, streamlining the ordering process and reducing wait times. Customers receive suggestions based on their history, enhancing convenience.

4. **In-Store Enhancements**

   RestTech goes beyond digital channels to improve in-store experiences. Self-order kiosks and digital menu boards provide real-time recommendations, speeding up service and increasing sales.

Overall, creating personalized experiences through utilizing the CDP not only enhances customer satisfaction but also drives revenue growth. By leveraging data and technology, QSRs can forge stronger connections with their customers, making each visit a unique and delightful experience.

Omnichannel Engagement that Seamlessly Connecting Touchpoints

An Omnichannel Engagement strategy seamlessly connects customer touchpoints to create a cohesive and personalized dining experience. This approach ensures that whether a customer interacts with the brand through mobile apps, websites, in-store kiosks, drive-thru lanes, or social media, they receive a consistent and tailored experience.

The following explores how CDPs facilitate an omnichannel approach:

1. **Unified Digital Brand Experience**
   This refers to omnichannel digital touchpoints that show consistent food menus, loyalty point redemption, and personalized information that resonate well with the customer. This applies to customers transacting via mobile app, kiosk, or any other digital channel.

2. **Introducing eKYC**
   To present a seamless and consistent brand experience, various digital channels must be able to recognize and provide the same level of services. As an example, a customer can earn and redeem their loyalty points in-store, on mobile apps, or on websites. It is therefore a good strategy for QSR to implement a customer digital identification infrastructure known as eKYC (Electronic Know Your Customers) that allows customers to sign in to any RestTech channel.

3. **Data Integration**
   The CDP platform integrates data from various touchpoints, only through this integration, customer activities such as targeted upselling and loyalty point collection can be carried out in any digital channel.

4. **Seamless Ordering**

Customers can order across any channel with the same unified brand experience and the ability to perform one-click re-ordering of their favorite if they are in a hurry, as CDP allows order history to be easily recalled.

5. **Personalization**

The strategy leverages customer data to offer personalized promotions, suggest menu items, and tailor loyalty rewards based on individual preferences.

With CDP, kiosks can identify customers through mobile app integration and QRCode. (Credit: KFC China)

Loyalty Programs and Customer Retention

Drilling deeper into customer retention strategy, QSRs can employ loyalty programs to incentivize repeat business, re-engage lapsed customers, and collect valuable customer data. These programs often offer rewards, discounts, or exclusive offers to members. CDPs play a vital role by aggregating customer data from various touchpoints. This consolidated data helps QSRs personalize loyalty program rewards based on individual preferences and behavior, increasing their effectiveness.

As for Customer Retention, retaining existing customers is often more cost-effective than acquiring new ones. CDPs enable QSRs to create data-driven customer retention strategies. By analyzing historical data, QSRs can identify loyal customers, understand their preferences, and engage them with personalized offers and promotions. Additionally, CDPs facilitate targeted communications through email, mobile notifications, and social media, keeping customers informed about new menu items, special deals, and events. Ultimately, by leveraging CDPs in loyalty programs and customer retention efforts, QSRs can build stronger, longer-lasting relationships with their customer base, drive repeat visits, and increase revenue.

Data Privacy and Compliance

In any CDP implementation strategy, data privacy and compliance are paramount. Protecting customers' data is not only an ethical obligation but also a legal requirement.

Data privacy involves safeguarding personal information collected by QSRs, such as customer name, payment details, and contact information. Compliance, on the other hand, entails adhering to relevant data protection laws and regulations.

Example data privacy laws around the world include:

- **General Data Protection Regulation (GDPR)**
  Enforced in the European Union, GDPR dictates strict rules for data collection, processing, and protection. QSRs operating in EU countries must ensure explicit consent for data usage and promptly report data breaches.
- **California Consumer Privacy Act (CCPA)**
  This US law grants California residents control over their data. QSRs with California customers must provide data transparency, the option to opt-out, and safeguards against discrimination.
- **Personal Information Protection Law (PIPL)**
  Recently enacted in China, PIPL regulates the collection and processing of personal information, imposing strict consent requirements and data localization rules on QSRs.
- **Malaysia's Personal Data Protection Act (PDPA)**
  The act was passed by the Parliament of Malaysia in 2010 to regulate the processing of personal data in commercial transactions.
- **Personal Data Protection Bill (PDPB)**
  India's proposed legislation aims to protect personal data, similar to GDPR. QSRs in India would need to adhere to data localization and privacy consent requirements.
- **Payment Card Industry – Data Security Standards (PCI-DSS)**
  It is a set of security standards designed to ensure that all companies that accept, process, store, or transmit credit card information maintain a secure environment. The PCI DSS was developed to protect sensitive cardholder data from theft and fraud. Failure to comply with PCI-DSS can result in financial penalties, legal consequences, and damage to a QSR's reputation.

Incorporating robust data privacy and compliance measures within a CDP strategy ensures that QSRs respect customer rights, mitigate legal risks, and build trust, all while leveraging customer data for improved services and experiences.

Implementation Challenges in CDP Strategy

- QSRs often struggle with data integration challenges from various sources like point-of-sale systems, mobile apps, and online orders into a unified CDP. This challenge can lead to incomplete or inaccurate customer profiles.
- Data privacy and compliance with regulations are paramount. Mishandling customer data can result in legal and reputational consequences.
- Many QSRs operate with legacy systems that may not seamlessly integrate with modern CDP solutions, causing implementation difficulties.

Best Practices in CDP Implementation

- Comprehensive data mapping and master data management are key. Begin by mapping all data sources and flows within your QSR. Identify the critical data touchpoints and establish data quality standards.
- Prioritize data security and implement robust security measures to protect customer data. Encryption, access controls, and regular security audits are essential. There are many data loss prevention security platforms in the market that one can deploy.
- Invest in training of staff on CDP usage, policy, and data handling practices.
- Implement the CDP in phases, starting with core functionalities. Some successful early adopters initially focused on loyalty program data integration before expanding their CDP capabilities.

- Customer consent is a must in the CDP policy and respect customer consent preferences and transparently communicate data usage. QSR must allow customers to manage their data preferences through any touchpoints.

By addressing these challenges and adhering to best practices, QSRs can successfully implement a CDP strategy like Starbucks. Starbucks' data-driven approach has enabled them to personalize offers, improve customer experiences, and drive customer loyalty through their loyalty program and mobile app.

Chapter 9:
The Role of Marketing Technology (MarTech)

In the dynamic landscape of QSRs, where competition is fierce and customer preferences rapidly evolve, the intersection of marketing and technology has become a strategic imperative. This chapter delves into the multifaceted world of Marketing Technology (MarTech), showcasing how leading QSR brands are leveraging advanced tools to connect with customers, enhance engagement, and drive business growth. The better-known MarTech applications are Content Management System (CMS), Customer Relationship Management (CRM), and Search Engine Optimization (SEO).

Personalization in Marketing with A Data-Driven Approach

MarTech leverages customer data obtained through various RestTech channels, such as kiosks, POS, mobile apps, online orders, and loyalty programs, to create personalized marketing campaigns. The purpose of rolling them out is mainly to analyze customer behavior, preferences, and purchase history to tailor promotions, offers, and messaging, ensuring they resonate with individual tastes.

For instance, MarTech can recommend menu items based on past orders, send targeted promotions during a customer's preferred dining hours, or even acknowledge special occasions like birthdays. This level of personalization enhances customer engagement and loyalty.

Furthermore, MarTech enables QSRs to monitor campaign performance in real time, adjusting strategies based on data insights. By combining RestTech and MarTech, QSRs can create a more meaningful and memorable dining experience, fostering stronger customer relationships and driving sales growth in the competitive QSR landscape.

Geotargeting and Location-Based Marketing

Geotargeting enables QSRs to deliver specific content and promotions to customers based on their geographical location. This technology leverages the customer's GPS data or CDP's home address to estimate their whereabouts, allowing QSRs to send relevant and timely messages. For instance, if a customer is near a QSR restaurant location, they might receive a notification from the QSR marketing with a special offer, encouraging them to visit the nearest restaurant which increases foot traffic and drives sales.

Location-based marketing takes geotargeting a step further by delivering personalized messages and promotions that are specific to a particular store's proximity. It enables QSRs to tailor their marketing efforts to match the preferences and behaviors of local customers. For example, the marketing department might send promotions for breakfast items to customers in an area with high morning foot traffic, optimizing marketing spending and increasing the likelihood of conversions.

AI-Powered Recommendation Engines

MarTech software with AI-powered recommendation engines is a standout component. These engines leverage data analytics and artificial intelligence to offer personalized suggestions and enhance the customer experience.

AI-Powered Recommendation Engines analyze customer data, including order history, customer profile, and preferences, to make real-time menu recommendations. QSR's RestTech platform with this capability allows for tailored menu suggestions, upsizing, and upselling. For instance, a customer ordering a burger might receive personalized recommendations for a complementary side dish or beverage.

These recommendation engines not only drive incremental sales but also improve customer ordering experience with proactive suggestions. They create a sense of personalization and convenience, making customers feel valued and understood.

Moreover, they provide valuable insights into customer behavior, helping marketing folks refine their menu offerings and marketing strategies. In the dynamic world of QSRs, AI-powered recommendation engines are a potent tool, aligning perfectly with RestTech's mission to streamline operations, drive sales, and enhance customer engagement.

Adobe Magento, a leading online commerce software solution, for instance, has an AI software feature known as Adobe Sensei to power product recommendations in their commerce suite.

In addition, a leading smart kiosk vendor, TabSquare, has an AI Engine "AIDEN" in their in-store and online ordering solution to empower QSR with product recommendations. Maximizing upsize and upsell opportunities during the customer ordering process.

Engaging Through Social Media and Influencers

Engaging Through Social Media

In the modern world, consumers are moving away from traditional print media, TV, and radio channels because of increasing tech literacy and widespread adoption of smart devices. Advertisers are now spending their media budget on personalized marketing channels such as social media.

MarTech enables QSRs to establish a strong presence on popular social media platforms such as TikTok, Facebook, Instagram, X, and YouTube. It facilitates targeted advertising, allowing QSRs to reach specific demographics with personalized content, promotions, and interactive campaigns. MarTech tools also provide valuable insights into customer sentiment and engagement metrics, helping QSRs tailor their social media strategies for maximum impact. Real-time monitoring allows rapid responses to customer feedback, ensuring a positive online reputation. Ultimately, MarTech empowers marketing departments to connect with their customer base, build brand loyalty, and drive sales frequency through compelling social media interactions.

Influencer Marketing

MarTech enables marketing folks to identify, engage, and collaborate with social media influencers whose audiences align with their target demographic. It streamlines influencer outreach, campaign management, and performance tracking. Leveraging influencers' reach and authenticity, QSRs can generate buzz around new menu items, promotions, or initiatives. By tracking influencer-driven engagement and sales,

MarTech provides actionable data to refine influencer partnerships and maximize return on investment.

MarTech is an invaluable tool for maximizing Return on Advertising Spent (ROAS), a key measurement of Performance Marketing.

Real-Time Feedback and Customer Interaction

MarTech elements such as Social Listening and Brand Monitoring Tools play a pivotal role in monitoring and managing the brand's social sentiments in social media.

Real-Time Feedback

MarTech tools enable QSRs to gather real-time feedback through various channels like mobile apps, self-service kiosks, and social media. This immediate feedback loop empowers restaurants to swiftly address customer concerns and make necessary improvements. Automated surveys and sentiment analysis tools process customer sentiments, providing valuable insights into service quality. This helps to capture and analyze people's opinions, enabling the QSR to react quickly to the information obtained.

Customer Interaction

MarTech facilitates personalized and interactive customer engagement. Through data analytics, marketing folks can tailor marketing messages and promotions based on individual preferences and behavior. Mobile apps and social media platforms enable direct communication with customers, fostering a sense of community and brand loyalty. Chatbots and virtual assistants provide instant answers to customer queries or guide them through the ordering process, enhancing efficiency and convenience.

Chapter 10:
Harnessing the Cloud Advantage

This chapter highlights the advantages of harnessing Cloud Platforms. Discover how leading brands are leveraging cloud technology to enhance flexibility, scalability, and data security, and streamline operations across their network of restaurants.

In an era defined by digital transformation, Cloud Platforms have emerged as essential tools for QSRs to streamline digital architecture and achieve unprecedented levels of scalability. Let's see how leading QSR brands are leveraging cloud advantage to drive innovation, efficiency, and growth.

The Evolution of RestTech with Cloud Platforms

Initially, QSRs relied on traditional, on-premises IT infrastructure, limiting their scalability and agility. Since the advent of cloud technology, this has become the push that the industry needs to surpass these limitations.

Cloud platforms have enabled QSRs' tech teams to scale resources up or down based on demand, ensuring uninterrupted service during peak hours. They have also brought cost efficiency, as QSRs only pay for the resources they consume, eliminating the need for costly physical IT infrastructure.

Furthermore, cloud technology has facilitated the integration of advanced data analytics, enhancing decision-making processes. QSRs can now gather and analyze vast amounts of data collected across wide geographies.

In this digital age, cloud platforms continue to empower innovation in QSRs for a very long term. From mobile apps to IoT devices, cloud technology has become the backbone of RestTech strategies, empowering super-scale QSRs like McDonald's and KFC to offer more convenience, efficiency, and data-driven insights to customers while staying competitive in a rapidly evolving industry.

Centralized Data and Unified Operations

Cloud platforms serve as centralized hubs for storing and managing vast amounts of data, including menu masters, customer orders, inventories, and sales data, across multiple restaurant locations.

This centralized data accessibility ensures consistency in menu offerings, pricing, and customer information. Real-time updates are easily disseminated to all branches, and all digital channels, eliminating discrepancies, and enhancing operational efficiency. A practical example of this would be customer information shared across all branches, so that any customer would be recognized whichever branch they visit, or menu pricing changes being updated to all branches together without the need for notifying all the branches individually.

Unified operations become achievable as cloud-based solutions facilitate synchronized processes. Inventory management, employee scheduling, and marketing campaigns can be coordinated seamlessly across all locations. This unified approach leads to standardized customer experiences, streamlined management, and data-driven decision-making.

Overall, the cloud's ability to centralize data and unify operations empowers QSRs to maintain consistency, improve efficiency, and enhance customer satisfaction across their entire network, ultimately driving success in the competitive QSR industry.

Enhanced Security and Data Protection
Cloud technology enhances security and data protection for QSRs in several ways.

Firstly, reputable cloud providers invest heavily in state-of-the-art security measures, including data encryption, data loss prevention, firewall protection, and intrusion detection systems. This expertise ensures that QSRs benefit from top-tier security features without the need for in-house specialists and infrastructure.

Secondly, cloud providers are required to meet stringent compliance standards and certifications, such as ISO 27001 and SOC 2, ensuring that data is handled securely and following industry regulations.

Additionally, cloud platforms offer robust access controls, allowing tech teams to manage and restrict who can access sensitive data. This helps prevent unauthorized access, both internally and externally.

Finally, cloud providers typically have disaster recovery and backup solutions through their Availability Zones Architecture, safeguarding QSRs against data loss due to unforeseen events.

By leveraging cloud technology, QSRs' tech teams can significantly enhance their security posture and data protection, enabling them to focus on delivering exceptional customer experiences while leaving the complexities of data security to industry experts.

Cloud-Based Point-of-Sale (POS) Systems
Cloud-based POS systems offer QSRs numerous advantages. It helps QSR's IT department to streamline the system

administration, enable remote management, and facilitate data-driven decision-making for efficient operations.

Firstly, they enhance operational efficiency by centralizing order processing, menu promotions, and pricing management. QSRs can instantly update menus, pricing, and promotions across all locations, ensuring consistency.

Secondly, cloud POS systems are highly scalable and can accommodate the fluctuating demands of a QSR, especially during peak hours. This scalability ensures fast and reliable order processing, reducing wait times for customers.

Moreover, cloud POS systems provide real-time data analytics, enabling QSRs to make data-driven decisions about inventory, staffing, and menu optimization. This improves overall kitchen cooking and staffing projection.

Lastly, cloud POS systems facilitate seamless integration with other digital platforms, such as online ordering and mobile apps, enabling QSRs to offer a truly omnichannel experience for their customers.

Best Practices!

For large-scale QSRs with hundreds or thousands of restaurants. It's always recommended to have a POS system that is cloud-enabled. However, it is equally important to have the same POS system that can function offline when the internet connection is down. This ensures restaurant business can go on in both online and offline modes.

Cost Optimization and Resource Management

Cloud platforms such as AWS and Microsoft Azure provide robust resource management tools, allowing QSRs to monitor and allocate computing resources precisely as needed. This flexibility ensures efficient performance during peak hours while being able to be scaled down during slower periods, reducing overall operational costs.

Furthermore, cloud analytics empower QSRs to gain insights into resource usage patterns, enabling data-driven decisions to further optimize costs and streamline IT operations. In essence, cloud technology offers a cost-effective and efficient solution for resource management for the tech team.

Chapter 11:
Implementation Strategy: Navigating Change

The adoption of RestTech solutions presents an exciting transformation for QSRs, but it also comes with its challenges. This chapter delves into the critical aspects of implementing RestTech effectively, where we will learn how successful QSR brands navigate vendor selection, staff training, change management, and more to ensure a seamless transition to a tech-driven model.

The Roadmap to RestTech Implementation

Implementing RestTech effectively begins with meticulous planning. This initial phase is indispensable for QSR owners and operators, as it sets the foundation for a successful digital transformation.

1. **Needs Assessment**

   The journey commences with a thorough assessment of your QSR's unique technology needs. Understand the specific areas where technology can make the most impact. Is it streamlining kitchen operations, enhancing the customer ordering experience, optimizing delivery logistics, or harnessing data for better decision-making? Identifying these needs will be pivotal in shaping your RestTech strategy.

2. **Goals and Objectives**

   Clearly defined goals and objectives are the guiding stars of your implementation strategy. These objectives should be closely tied to your overall business strategy and customer expectations. Are you aiming to boost sales, reduce operational costs, enhance customer satisfaction, or expand your market reach? The answers to these questions will drive the rest of your RestTech planning.

3. **Budgeting and Resource Allocation**

   Once you have a clear understanding of your needs and objectives, allocate a budget that supports your RestTech endeavors. This budget should encompass not only the cost of acquiring and implementing technology but also the financial resources needed for staff training, ongoing maintenance, and potential unforeseen expenses. Effective budgeting ensures that your RestTech journey remains financially sustainable.

4. **Business Prioritization**

   Due to limited budget and resources, QSR's owner needs to prioritize the digitalization in phases. Focusing on revenue uplift components and followed by cost optimization ones. This may be a multi-year investment strategy.

In essence, this planning phase is the blueprint for your RestTech transformation. It ensures that you embark on this journey with a comprehensive understanding of your QSR's technology needs, well-defined goals, and the financial resources necessary for a successful implementation. It's the essential groundwork that paves the way for the digital evolution of your QSR, ensuring that you can harness technology to its fullest potential.

Vendor Selection and Partnerships

Choosing the right tech vendors and forging strategic partnerships is a critical step in the successful implementation of RestTech. The process involves a meticulous evaluation of potential vendors to ensure they align with the QSR's specific needs and objectives.

Firstly, it's essential to identify vendors with a proven track record in the QSR industry, as they possess a deep understanding of the unique challenges and requirements of fast-food businesses. Assess their technology offerings, scalability, and compatibility with existing systems to ensure a seamless integration process.

Furthermore, consider the vendor's commitment to ongoing support and maintenance, as technology in QSRs requires continuous monitoring and updates. Establish clear communication channels and service level agreements to guarantee timely assistance in case of issues.

Strategic partnerships can also be leveraged to drive RestTech success. Collaborate with technology providers, industry peers, and startups to access innovative solutions and shared insights. These partnerships can accelerate RestTech adoption and offer access to a broader ecosystem of solutions.

Staff Training and Change Management

Imagine rolling a technology solution to a QSR with thousands of crews spread across numerous restaurant locations, it is an uphill task for QSR operators to do so. Staff training and change management are pivotal components in ensuring successful implementation. Incorporating these strategies ensures that staff are well-prepared and motivated, minimizing disruptions and maximizing the benefits of RestTech implementation in the QSR industry.

1. **Training**
   Comprehensive staff training programs should be tailored to specific RestTech solutions. These programs equip

employees with the skills needed to operate new technology effectively. Training should be ongoing to keep staff up to date with evolving systems. Market and regional coaches need to be put in place to provide ongoing training and support for staff operating in restaurants to embrace and utilize the technology as intended.

2. **Change Management**
Managing change involves transparent communication about the reasons for implementing RestTech and its benefits. Involving staff in the process, addressing concerns, and providing a support system during the transition are crucial. Encouraging a culture of adaptability and learning ensures that staff not only embrace the change but also contribute to its success.

3. **Franchisees Onboarding**
For large QSR operators with a network of franchisees, it is important to engage and onboard their franchisees upfront. Have them involved in the early stage and pilot to have their participation, inclusion, and buy-in for subsequent rollout investments.

Managing Resistance to Change

Implementing new technology components often encounters resistance from restaurant employees and stakeholders. To ensure a successful transition, it's vital to effectively manage this resistance.

1. **Communication**

   Clear, transparent, and consistent communication is key. Explain the reasons for the change, its benefits, and how it aligns with the QSR's goals. Address concerns openly and provide a platform for feedback.

2. **Involvement**

   Involve employees in the decision-making process. Solicit the restaurant users and operators' input, listen to their ideas, and make them feel like active participants in the change. This not only fosters ownership but also generates innovative   solutions.

3. **Training and Support**

   Comprehensive training programs are essential. Equip staff with the skills and knowledge they need to navigate the new technology confidently. Provide ongoing support to address issues   and   concerns   as   they   arise.

4. **Leadership**

   Strong leadership is crucial. C-level leaders such as the CEO should embody the change, set an example, and demonstrate enthusiasm for the RestTech adoption. Their commitment   inspires   confidence   among   employees.

5. **Celebrate Successes**

   Recognize and celebrate small victories along the way. Acknowledge and reward those who embrace the change and contribute positively to its implementation.

Managing resistance to change ensures that employees and stakeholders not only accept RestTech but also become advocates for its success. This collaborative approach paves the way for a smoother transition and maximizes the benefits of technology adoption in QSRs.

Pilot Restaurant Trial Before Market Rollout

New technology rollout may face teething issues and challenges in the live restaurant environment that may not be obvious in lab testing. It is, therefore, wise to conduct a pilot restaurant test in a controlled environment before market-wide rollout to hundreds or thousands of restaurants. This gives the tech team the ability to fix any technical and operational issues, perfecting the solution before scaling up. Provide seamless and frictionless technology transition.

Chapter 12:
The Future of Food Delivery in the QSR Industry

This chapter takes us on a journey into the future of the QSR industry powered by RestTech. It exploits emerging trends such as AI-powered chatbots, robotics, virtual reality dining experiences, sustainable technologies, and more that promise to reshape the QSR landscape. Stay ahead of the curve and prepare for the exciting possibilities that lie ahead.

The evolution of the QSR industry has extended beyond physical dining spaces to include the dynamic realm of food delivery, made relevant post-COVID-19 pandemic where consumers have shifted online and increasing reliance on food delivery. Based on my experience in the QSR industry while navigating through the pandemic, it is observed that an increasing number of consumers are trending toward online channels. As technology continues to reshape the way we dine, the food delivery system has become a critical component of the QSR landscape. We'll explore how forward-looking QSR brands are leveraging technology to revolutionize the food delivery experience.

Delivery Apps

The rise of food delivery apps has significantly altered the dining landscape. Leading QSR brands have developed robust food delivery systems to ensure maximum coverage, using their delivery apps to provide customers with a seamless ordering and delivery experience. These apps offer menu browsing, customization, and real-time tracking, ensuring customers have visibility of the food delivery status while they are waiting for their food.

Contactless Delivery and Safety Measures

In response to global pandemic events, contactless delivery has emerged as a priority for food service sectors. Through technology, QSRs are offering customers the option to receive their orders without any physical contact, minimizing health risks and ensuring a safe dining experience.

Based on literature reviews conducted, Yum! Brands China is the first QSR group that "invented" the term "Contactless Delivery" during the COVID-19 pandemic. This innovative food safety protocol helps to curtail the spread of the virus while creating a positive safe dining experience for consumers.

Delivery Efficiency and Logistics

Technology has enabled QSRs to optimize their delivery logistics. Through route optimization algorithms, real-time traffic data, and GPS tracking, QSRs can ensure timely deliveries and reduce delivery times. This not only enhances customer satisfaction but also contributes to operational efficiency. In the larger context, it helps QSR to contribute to the Environmental, Social, and Governance (ESG) policies through lesser CO_2 emissions from their food logistics. This is a crucial consumer consideration of the brand's corporate ethics moving forward.

The Rise of Dark Kitchens

A "dark kitchen" in the QSR industry refers to a kitchen concept designed exclusively for fulfilling delivery and online orders. Unlike a traditional dine-in restaurant, a dark kitchen operates with minimal or no physical storefronts. It primarily focuses on efficiently preparing and dispatching meals for delivery, making it a strategic response to the growing demand for online food ordering. Dark kitchens allow QSR to expand the food delivery network and serve new markets. They leverage RestTech to streamline operations, serving as an innovative and cost-effective solution to meet the evolving preferences of the digital-savvy consumer. Navigating into the future, the dark kitchen model is crucial, especially for the rapidly changing landscape of food service.

Drone and Autonomous Vehicle Delivery

As technology continues to advance, tech savvy QSRs are exploring the potential of drone and autonomous vehicle delivery. These innovations promise to further accelerate delivery times and open new possibilities for reaching remote locations and densely populated areas. However, the drone battery limitation, regulatory challenges, and immaturity of drone technology at the moment are restrictions and hence require more R&D investment.

Drone delivery of pizza by the Domino's pilot trial run in the Netherlands. (Source: www.livemint.com)

Robotic pizza delivery is being tested in Vancouver.
(Source: www.vancouverisawesome.com)

KFC rolls out self-driving food trucks in China using 5G autonomous vehicles.
(Source: www.cnet.com)

The potential of unmanned food trucks is on the rise.

The Continuous Evolution of Future Delivery

As the RestTech journey unfolds, the future of food delivery promises to be one of continuous evolution. From exploring new delivery methods to enhancing customer engagement through personalized recommendations, the QSR industry is on the cusp of delivering experiences that transcend physical boundaries and embrace the digital age, this is made possible by the imagination of innovators in the industry.

In the intricate tapestry of RestTech, the food delivery system stands as a testament to the industry's adaptability and innovation. As leading QSRs continue to harness technology to redefine convenience, safety, and accessibility, the future of food delivery is bound to be as exciting and transformative as the journey that has brought us here.

Chapter 13:
The Future Trends of RestTech

As the QSR industry continues its digital transformation journey, the future holds even more exciting possibilities. As we speak, while the industry is adopting RestTech 1.0, the possibility of RestTech 2.0 is on the horizon. Possible future tech like big data, IoTs, artificial intelligence, machine learning, virtual reality dining experiences, robotic kitchens, sustainable technologies, and beyond.

This final chapter explores emerging trends and innovations that are poised to revolutionize the QSR landscape. We also highlight case studies of such adoptions that should inspire us in our RestTech journey.

Unmanned Kitchens of the Future

A leading tech innovator, Pizza Hut Israel is on the brink of a groundbreaking transformation with the emergence of unmanned kitchens, a concept that redefines the way fast food is prepared and served. Imagine a kitchen where robots and automation take center stage, orchestrating culinary symphonies with precision and consistency.

Pizza Hut Israel provides a glimpse into this future. Pizza Hut Israel President Udi Shamai unveiled a fully automated pizza preparation robotic system. This robot is equipped to knead dough, apply sauces, and add toppings, all with remarkable accuracy. Such innovations not only streamline operations but also ensure the highest quality and consistency in every pizza.

The possibilities are vast. Unmanned kitchens reduce ever-increasing labor costs, enhance hygiene, and, most importantly, allow QSRs to meet the growing demand for contactless and fast dining experiences. As technology continues to evolve, we can expect unmanned kitchens to play a pivotal role in shaping the future of QSRs, offering unparalleled efficiency and customization while maintaining the delicious flavors customers love.

Unmanned pizza restaurant by Pizza Hut. (Credit: Pizza Hut Israel)

Pizza perfection is made entirely by robots. An Innovation by Pizza Hut Israel.
(Source: nocamels.com)

AI-powered Chatbots and Voice Assistants

AI-powered voice chatbot and AI voice assistant such as Alexa has huge potential in the future digital design of QSR. These latest AI technologies promise to revolutionize customer service, streamline operations, and enhance the overall brand experience.

- **Chatbots for Seamless Ordering**

  AI-powered chatbots will become more intuitive and capable of handling complex orders. Customers can place orders, customize meals, and get real-time menu recommendations through chat, making the ordering process smoother and more personalized.

- **Voice Assistants for Hands-Free Ordering**
  Voice-activated assistants like Amazon's Alexa or Google Assistant will allow customers to place orders simply by speaking. This hands-free approach will be invaluable for in-car ordering and home automation. This convenience further blurs the lines between physical and digital brand experiences.

Alexa voice ordering channel by KFC India.
(Source: timesofindia.indiatimes.com)

KFC India, for instance, has deployed an innovative Alexa voice ordering channel to assist customers with orders, providing an unparalleled convenient, and interactive way to order their favorite meals.

As AI and voice recognition technologies continue to advance, QSRs embracing these innovations will not only increase operational efficiency but also create more engaging and personalized interactions with customers, solidifying their position in the ever-evolving consumer landscape.

Virtual Reality (VR) and Augmented Reality (AR) Dining Experiences

The future of QSRs brand experience promises to be an immersive and interactive one with the integration of Virtual Reality (VR) and Augmented Reality (AR) dining experiences. VR and AR technologies will play a pivotal role in transforming how customers engage with the brands.

- **Virtual Reality (VR) Dining Experiences**

  Imagine putting on a VR gadget at a QSR and instantly being transported to a virtual world where you can dine in any setting of your choice. For instance, a restaurant could offer customers the opportunity to enjoy their meal in a virtual beachfront setting, complete with the sound of waves and seagulls. Another scenario is while waiting for food to be served, customers can virtually tour the restaurant's kitchen, getting a behind-the-scenes look at food preparation. This enhances transparency and fosters a sense of connection with the brand. This immersive experience adds an entirely new dimension to dining, enhancing customers with a "Wow-some" experience.

- **Augmented Reality (AR) Enhancements**

  AR, on the other hand, will superimpose digital elements onto the real-world dining experience. QSRs can use AR to provide interactive menus where customers can point their smartphones at a menu item to view detailed information, nutritional facts, ingredients, or customer reviews. Also, AR can be used to gamify the dining experience while waiting for food, turning every meal into an adventure. Rewarding customers for engaging with the brand through AR technology.

Sustainability and Green Technologies

In line with growing consumers' environmental awareness, QSRs need to be forefront of embracing sustainability and green technologies. QSRs can use RestTech to showcase to customers their sustainability efforts and foster better brand trust, particularly with consumers who are very environmentally conscious. Here are some of the key takeaways:

1. IoT sensors and AI-control smart kitchens will improve energy efficiency. These green technologies will transform restaurant operations. Energy-efficient kitchen appliances, LED screens, and smart IoT devices that control optimum temperature in the freezer and chillers within the back of the house.

2. AI and data analytics to improve kitchen cook projection systems will help QSRs optimize their menus to reduce food waste by predicting demand more accurately.

3. Blockchain-enabled food supply chain system will ensure food traceability that will enable QSRs to track the sourcing of ingredients, improving ethical, sustainable practices and building brand trust.

4. Using rider navigation apps for last-mile food delivery fleets, and electric vehicles, along with optimized route planning using GPS, will minimize the carbon footprint of food deliveries.

Hyper-Personalization through AI and Data Insights

The future of consumer brand preference lies in hyper-personalization, a dynamic made possible through the synergy of AI and data insights. AI algorithms, fueled by extensive data mining and analysis, will enable QSRs to offer customers unprecedented levels of tailored experiences.

1. **Individualized Recommendations**

   AI-driven systems will understand customers' preferences, ordering history, and even contextual factors like weather or time of day. This depth of insight will result in menu recommendations perfectly aligned with each customer's tastes.

2. **Adaptive Menu Selections**

   Menus will adapt in real-time. For instance, a vegetarian customer may see entirely plant-based options, while a pizza lover might encounter pizza-centric choices, all within the same menu interface.

3. **Streamlined Ordering and Payment**

   AI will make the ordering process smoother. It can predict when customers are likely to order and have their preferred items ready for seamless one-click purchases.

4. **Targeted Marketing**

   AI-driven marketing campaigns will be highly targeted. Customers will receive messages that align with their tastes, ordering habits, and even their physical location. These will lead to higher potential returns on advertising spend (ROAS).

As AI and data insights evolve, QSRs will be at the forefront of a culinary revolution, offering not just food, but deeply personalized dining experiences. Hyper-personalization will strengthen customer engagement and position QSRs as leaders in the competitive restaurant industry of the future.

Conclusion:
Revolutionizing Quick Service Restaurants

The QSR industry has undergone a remarkable transformation fueled by the integration of RestTech solutions. From omnichannel experiences to advanced kitchen systems, data-driven strategies, and innovative marketing technologies, QSRs have harnessed the power of technology to deliver unparalleled customer experiences, streamline operations, and drive growth. As we conclude this journey through the digital landscape of QSRs, several key insights and takeaways emerge.

Bring the Omnichannel Together

Connecting every digital touchpoint, RestTech has shattered the barriers between the physical and digital worlds, enabling QSRs to seamlessly engage customers across various touchpoints. The convergence of mobile apps, self-service kiosks, online ordering platforms, and in-store technology has created a cohesive dining journey that caters to customers' preferences for convenience and personalization.

Best Practices!

As RestTech involves many digital components, integrating them to work in a well-orchestrated manner is a challenging task. It is strongly recommended that the tech team of QSRs invest in a robust open API platform, serving as a centralized powerhouse for executing diverse API calls for connecting various RestTech software components.

Data as the Driving Force to Create Customer Insights

Central to RestTech's success is the strategic utilization of data. QSRs have tapped into the wealth of customers' information to understand behaviors, preferences, and trends. This data-driven approach has fueled personalized experiences, operational optimizations, and the creation of effective loyalty programs that foster brand loyalty and drive revenue growth.

Operational Excellence Though Smart Kitchens

In the heart of QSR operations, advanced kitchen systems have transformed the way food is prepared and delivered. Automation, real-time synchronization, and inventory management have minimized errors, improved consistency, and accelerated service, ultimately enhancing customer experience and satisfaction.

Building Bridges through Scalable and Secure Cloud Platforms

The cloud has emerged as a bedrock for QSR success, offering scalability, flexibility, and security. Brands have leveraged cloud technology to streamline operations, centralize data, and enhance customer experiences. Cloud-based point-of-sale systems have simplified transactions, while robust security measures have safeguarded customer and business data.

People and Technology in Harmony

As QSRs embraced RestTech solutions, the critical role of implementation strategy came to the forefront. The transition to new technologies required careful planning, vendor selection, staff training, and change management. Successful QSRs have not only adopted RestTech but also cultivated a culture of adaptation and innovation among their teams.

A Glimpse into Tomorrow, The Uncharted Horizon

As we peer into the future of RestTech, exciting trends emerge. Big data, machine learning, AI-powered chatbots, voice AI, large language models, virtual reality dining experiences, sustainable technologies, blockchain-enabled food traceability, IoT, and hyper-personalization through AI and data insights are poised to reshape the QSR landscape.

In this dynamic and ever-evolving environment, QSRs that embrace innovation, stay attuned to customer preferences, and boldly integrate RestTech solutions will continue to thrive. The RestTech revolution has redefined the way QSRs engage with their customers, transform their operations, and shape the future of dining experiences. As the journey continues, remember that the digital culinary frontier is a canvas of endless possibilities.

RestTech is reshaping the QSR industry, offering new avenues for growth, efficiency, and customer engagement. The future of quick-service dining is here, and it's digital.

Best Practices!

Although RestTech is at the forefront of revolutionizing quick-service restaurants, QSR owners must not forget that the essence of the brand's customer emotional connection is still human. Therefore, when architecting a brand's digital touchpoints, the human element must be visible as part of the overall brand's experience.

References:
Restaurant Technology Vendors

The following is a list of RestTech solution providers for reference.

RestTech Solution Providers	Solution Briefs
Acrelec acrelec.com	Specializes in customer experience technology solutions, particularly in the restaurant and QSR industries such as kiosks and drive-thru.
Adobe Commerce business.adobe.com	Adobe Commerce is a commerce platform that offers a powerful e-commerce solution that provides businesses with a wide range of tools and features to create, manage, and optimize online stores. It offers a flexible and customizable platform that can cater to the needs of businesses of all sizes, from small startups to large QSR businesses.
CMG Group www.cmg.com.my	Integrated restaurant tech solutions from omnichannel to POS to kitchen systems to order management.
DragonTail Systems www.dragontail.com	A restaurant kitchen management system with a sophisticated algorithm that manages the entire process starting from food preparation to its delivery to the customer, completely streamlining the food

	preparation and delivery processes.
Evoke www.evoke-creative.com	Evoke works with some of the leading QSR brands such as McDonald's, in developing and deploying kiosk solutions that transform the entire customer journey.
FingerMark fingermark.ai	Their Connected Restaurant solution helps QSR like KFC to integrate different areas.
Food Market Hub www.foodmarkethub.com	Restaurant procurement and inventory management platform that streamlines restaurant back-of-house processes.
HP Engage www.hp.com	Retail and Industry point of sales solutions.
Longbow www.longbow.com.my	Mobile ordering and self-service kiosk solution.
LG Commercial Display www.lg.com	Global giant for digital signage and touchscreen display.
NCR www.ncr.com	NCR Retail is offering everything you need in an easy-to-use platform, with kitchen solutions, digital ordering, reporting and analytics, and management tools.
Oracle Simphony POS www.oracle.com	The Simphony POS system from Oracle is built for complete restaurant management. As an all-in-one cloud POS platform, it helps restaurateurs optimize their online and in-house operations in real-time from any device.

Posiflex www.posiflex.com	Posiflex POS system is marketed worldwide as one of the leading brands in the industry.
Samsung Commercial Display www.samsung.com	World leader in digital signage, touchscreen displays, and outdoor displays for drive-thru applications.
SAP Commerce www.sap.com	The SAP Commerce Cloud solution provides an e-commerce platform that can help you innovate at scale and tap enterprise-wide data.
Summit Innovations summitqsr.com	A leader in QSR drive-thru and customer management systems. With advanced world-class technology and is trusted by some of the biggest QSR brands across the globe.
TabSquare tabsquare.ai	A full stack technology platform for QSR, spanning across all customer channels, in-store & online, and connecting them seamlessly to back-office operations.
Xilnex www.xilnex.com	Xilnex has empowered more than 5,000 retail merchants across Southeast Asia with innovative POS, one of the pioneer cloud-based POS solutions in the region.

Disclaimer:

The author is not associated with nor has any marketing affiliation with these companies, although the author may have engaged them in the previous or current RestTech journey. Their names are provided solely as a reference as they have successful deployments in the QSR industry.

The End.

This book sets the gold standard for Restaurant Technology (RestTech). In an era where technology drives Quick Service Restaurants (QSR), this book is a compass for food & beverage operators, innovators, digital transformation professionals, and enthusiasts alike. It defines RestTech standards, guiding QSR professionals to harness the power of digitalization, data, and innovation. The author's wealth of experience, spanning global multi-national giants and iconic QSR brands, forms the cornerstone for a comprehensive guide that promises to reshape the way the industry leverages technology and data. This book isn't just a reference; it's a roadmap for QSR or any retail pioneers ready to embark on a digital revolution.

Made in United States
Troutdale, OR
02/27/2024

17825979R10082